The
Common
Scents of
Smell

The World Publishing Company
Cleveland and New York

Russell C. Erb

The Common Scents of Smell

How the nose knows and what it all shows!

Published by The World Publishing Company
2231 West 110th Street, Cleveland, Ohio 44102
Published simultaneously in Canada by
Nelson, Foster & Scott Ltd.

First Printing 1968

Library of Congress Catalog Card Number: 68–13710

Printed in the United States of America

To Julia, my Wife and Sweetheart,
Two fine women

Contents

The Common Scents of Smell

1!
Osmics

ARE YOU TROUBLED with elephants running over your premises, your lawn and gardens? This can be annoying, but hope is in sight. Get yourself a few camels. The pesky elephants will leave, scurrying (if that's what elephants do) to other lawns in the neighborhood. Of course, you may then be stuck with a camel problem.

Elephants, it is said, just hate the smell of camels. So they go to places where the odor is more to their liking.

This is but one example—even though not a very likely one—of how important a place smell occupies in the life of living things. Without a sense of smell, the elephants would not have run away. Smell, like the elephant, is a big topic, and without a sense of smell, you and your friends would act a lot differently than you do (though I'm not sure how you really do act).

Humans use their sense of smell to determine what they like or dislike. Many delightful tales have been told about celebrating gentlemen of gay Paris drinking champagne from the slipper of a fair damsel. That is not as crazy as it sounds. Actually the drink is improved for a very logical reason. The leather of the slipper is nitrogenous, which accentuates the flavor and aroma of the beverage. After pouring the champagne into the shoe, always drink from the heel end. Otherwise, the toe point might stick into your Adam's apple. Drinking beer from an old boot might be just as good, as long as you trust the last person who wore it.

The case of the elephants and the camels was an illustration of the power of smells to repel, but there are certain odors to which we are magnetically drawn. Were you ever successful in passing by the waffle stand at a fair? According to Joseph N. Kane in his book *Famous First Facts*, the ice-cream cone was invented at the St. Louis Exposition in 1904 because a young lady was irresistibly attracted by the aroma of waffles. She visited a stand so frequently to buy ice-cream-and-waffle sandwiches that the young salesman, Charles E. Menches, began dating her after working hours.

To make an impression, he always brought her flowers and an ice-cream sandwich. One evening, lacking a vase for the flowers, she took one layer of the sandwich and rolled it into the form of a cone to act as a vase. The remaining layer was rolled in a similar manner to hold the ice cream.

The next day the clever youth introduced the novel idea at his stand and it was an instant success.

If the camels would only bathe in some perfumed pool before invading the elephants' territory, maybe the results would be different. Pleasant aromas not only influence our outward behavior but affect our reactions in other ways.

A chemist named Albert J. Dillinger found that the smell of magnolia blossoms blown around a dining room via the air-conditioner makes people hungrier and causes food to taste better. At home, we never keep magnolias in our dining room when guests are invited; it is more economical not to. When your appetite is dragging, or sagging, or lagging, have someone blow the floral aroma in your face. You will get either very hungry, or very sick. Maybe it would work just as well if you kept a pot of magnolias on the window sill of your dining area.

If someone wanted to make a study of why the camel smells like it does, the study would be called *osmics*. That's just a fancy name for the science of smell. It may be a new word to you, but it was thought up by a Greek more than three thousand years ago. An *osmatic* is one who has a normal sense of smell, but someone who can detect no odor at all is an *anosmatic*.

Of all the senses that we have been given, smell has received the least attention, yet it is one of the most primitive and one of the most important. "You smell" may have two meanings, but the mechanism of smelling is little understood.

The stimuli of seeing, hearing, and feeling are physical in nature. The physical stimulus for light and color may make us see blue under one condition and red under another. If we fail to see red when we should, we may get a traffic-violation ticket. In seeing, then, we are responding to the physical stimulus of light waves.

When a bell rings, we may answer the phone unless, of course, it is the doorbell. When a fighter fails to hear the bell, he is no longer responsive to physical stimuli including the stimulus of sound. Not many railroad grade crossings exist today, but where they still do, there are danger warnings that alert the eye and the ear. The stop signs and flashing red lights are augmented by a clanging gong. Maybe traffic safety experts could take a lesson from this by installing similar gongs at dangerous intersections to clang with every light change.

If someone punches me on the nose, I get the feeling of pain and also the feeling that he doesn't like me particularly. (Besides that, I get the feeling of embarrassment.) Here, I am responding to the stimuli of pressure, trauma, heat, and other physical excitants.

Sight, hearing, and feeling (or touch) are listed as physical senses. Mountains of books have been written about them as a result of countless experiments and ever-increasing research. These senses can be measured, recorded, duplicated, catalogued, and computerized.

Smell, and its closely related sense of taste, is a bouncing baby as far as study is concerned. It has not yet been properly measured, recorded, duplicated, catalogued, or computerized. It is an infant science, with growing pains and in need of many changes. One thing is known—smell and taste are due to chemical stimuli. Would you believe it— they are the only truly chemical senses?

Odors are all around you, on you, and in you. There is not a second of your life that some scent does not influence your behavior. You may want to run away from it, or you may want to embrace it (especially if it is on an attractive person). You may want to eat it, drink it, or inhale it. But no matter where you go or what you do, you cannot escape smells.

If you are an ordinary, average person, you should be able to smell two thousand different odors. With a little training and persistence, you can learn to differentiate about four thousand different smells. More than thirty thousand of our chemical compounds have an odor, ten thousand of which can be identified somehow. Some are so powerful that as little as one ten-millionth of a gram of the substance can affect your sniffing nose. That's about one hundredth of the size of the dot you put over the "i" when you write the word "little."

Olfaction is most efficient in people who are nonsmokers, especially women. If you are a male, remember that that old girl friend of yours can sniff and identify things that you cannot. When you call on her, you had better come clean. She can easily detect any trace of halitosis or under-arm perspiration. We boys can't smell her bodily emanations nearly as well. Of course, she doctors her shoulders and other strategic parts of her anatomy with odoriferous material liberally and deliberately so that you will find her a pleasing, good-smelling person.

2!
The Classification
of Smells

A SMELL is either pleasant or unpleasant. That is one way of classifying odors—not a good method, but an easy method. To the elephant, the smell of a camel is unpleasant, and to a horse, the smell of an elephant is too. Likewise, a particular smell may be agreeable to some people and disagreeable to others at the same time. Nevertheless, scientists sometimes overlook this fact and classify smells by

16

their pleasantness. They call this mysterious method of classifying *hedonics.*

Naming odors as either pleasant or unpleasant is a computer-like system of listing the various smells being experienced, and is probably used more extensively than any other method. However, the many factors creeping into this system result in many inaccuracies.

For example, color has a lot to do with whether you like or dislike a smell. Consider orangeade—you buy a glass full of that good, old yellow-orange fluid. You smell it, and it smells somewhat like oranges, largely because it has an orange color. But, if you took the color away and substituted a green for the orange, it might no longer smell or even taste like orange juice. In like manner, white licorice candy would not be recognized as licorice. We demand black, and the blacker, the better.

Beer must have that customary nut-brown color. A purple beer would not go over or down very well. We have been conditioned to associate brownness with the pleasant smell and taste of beer.

For a perfume to be marketable, it must be either amber or brown, regardless of the scent. If a popular fragrance were given an unaccustomed color, say blue, the demand for it would immediately diminish. It is a peculiar thing that the sense of color has this strong effect on whether a smell is agreeable or not. But it is true.

One time, I wanted to make my own brand of vanilla extract for my wife, so I got some vanillin, an organic compound that smells and tastes like vanilla because it is obtained from the real vanilla bean. It is a white powder. I then dissolved some of it in ethyl alcohol, the grain alcohol used for strong alcoholic beverages, and put the potent stuff into an ordinary glass bottle with an ordinary cork stopper.

It was a water-clear solution with a strong smell and taste of vanilla. As to the alcoholic content, it topped any of the strongest cocktails. It was really good stuff. I put a label on the bottle that said VANILLA loud and clear. Then I took it home. My wife looked at it, but said nothing—so loudly that I knew my product was not being accepted.

After several weeks, I asked her why she was not using my homemade flavoring. Her answer came quickly: "Oh, you and your vanilla." Translated, it meant that my prize product for home consumption was doomed. Yet, it was very good and very strong. A drop or two of the concoction would do the work of a teaspoon of commercial extract.

Maybe, I thought, the clearness and lack of color was not appealing. So, I burnt some sugar to caramelize it and dumped some into the bottle of MY VANILLA. Now it looked brown, like the store variety. Still my wife refused to use it! Maybe the bottle looked too laboratoryish, too much like the reagent bottles she had seen. I hit upon a sinister plan! One night, when she was attending some meeting and the coast at home was clear, I rummaged through the trash container and luckily found an empty bottle of a well-known brand of vanilla extract. I filled it with my product and put the bottle where the other flavoring extracts were being housed. It worked! She used it! She thought it was good but stronger than the last bottle she had used.

The same thing happened several years ago when I made a perfume and had to put it into an empty bottle of a popular brand of perfume before it was accepted. It all goes to prove that the container often makes the substance smell better than it really is. Sometimes perfumers spend more money on the container than on the contents, more thought to the cut than to the cloth. Any manufacturer can put cheap things into beautiful containers and get a better effect.

The name on the label has much to do with it too. "Kiss Me" is a daring, challenging name, especially if you want that act to be carried out. "Tease Me," a beefsteak aroma, may be the gateway to a man's heart. "Tabu"—well, you need a fiddle for that one.

Yes, this hedonic business is full of errors.

I gave a special test to a group of about 450 boys and girls, all pupils in the ninth grade of a public school. I asked them whether certain odors were agreeable or disagreeable to them. The results were as follows. (The figures are percentages of the boys tested and percentages of the girls tested respectively, not percentages of the mixed group.)

STIMULUS	AGREEABLE	
	Boys	*Girls*
1. Cigar smoke. (I wonder if any of the girls who didn't like the smell of a cigar will marry cigar smokers.)	31.6%	23.5%
2. Newly mown hay	94.8%	80.4%
3. Camphor	26.3%	59.9%
4. Frying onions	71.4%	24.1%
5. Cloves	78.8%	98.0%
6. Vanilla	100 %	100 %
7. Cheese (Swiss)	84.2%	39.2%
8. Leather (pocketbooks, purses)	23.5%	52.9%
9. Rubber	10.5%	38.4%
10. Coffee. (Girls are not quite the best coffee-makers.)	100 %	90.0%
11. Ammonia	1.0%	21.5%
12. Burning leaves	15.7%	40.5%

Stimulus		Agreeable
13. Tar	27.7%	68.9%
14. Rain on a dusty road	55.8%	60.3%
15. Woody odor of a sawmill	42.3%	81.0%

The poet James Whitcomb Riley once wrote:

How slight a thing may set one's fancy drifting
Upon the dead sea of the Past!— A view—
Sometimes an odor—or a rooster lifting
A far-off "Ooh! ooh-ooh!"

And suddenly we find ourselves astray
In some wood's-pasture of the Long Ago—
Or idly dream again a day
Of rest we used to know.

Our olfaction is tied to our past with unbreakable bonds. Some odors stir up memories so nostalgic that our mood can be completely altered. In the silent-film days, music was used to create moods for the actors, but with the advent of sound, this became impossible. To their delight, directors discovered that flooding the studio with a favorite aroma would stimulate some of the stars. Bing Crosby could make love more realistically with the scent of heliotrope, Martha Raye was more comical if she smelled geranium, and mint vapors were sprayed around at 4:00 P.M. to revive the lagging energies of the performers.

The olfactory nerve carries its findings directly to the seat of logic, memory, and imagination in the brain; thus associations help to influence the sensation of smell. In fact, there is a perfume on the market called "Nostalgia." You may want to smell the aroma of something gone by, but not the garbage truck, as a rule. If the years were rotten years, you wouldn't want to re-smell them. For Christmas time, you insist on the customary fragrance of pine needles. When I was a kid, I anticipated the aroma of oranges since this was the only time I would get such a delicacy. To this day, oranges make me think of tinkle-bells and jingle-bells and a Happy New Year. If we could only distill the joy of Christmas and put the essence into a bottle!

But, as we have said, this hedonic system is too unreliable to be a very good means of classifying smells.

You can also classify odors by saying, "It smells like ——." Your brain fills in the blank space. "It smells like a gardenia," you may say—unless you're sniffing brandy. So the question, "How does a gardenia smell?" is answered by, "It smells like a gardenia." Educationally, you don't seem to be getting anywhere. In this system you associate what you smell with past experience, but if you lack past experience, the gardenia might smell like anything or nothing.

A number of people, myself among them, have made attempts at odor classification. My classification consisted of four basic odors plus infra-odors and ultra-odors. The infra-odors are those which, by their strength and pungency, produce distracting sensations, even pain, probably due to chemical reaction. The ultra-odors are so feeble that normally they do not register on humans, at least not until a newer model of the nose is made. If ultra-odors are to be detected at all, they must have an extremely high concentration.

The four basic, or "primary," odors I listed were: (1) Fragrant, (2) Burnt, (3) Caprylic (Goaty), and (4) Acid or Sour. Crocker and Henderson also named these same four primary odors, but in a different order, and in their classification they listed degrees of strength under each category, in increasing order from 0 to 8, as follows:

Fragrant	Burnt	Caprylic	Acid
0	0	0	0
1	1	1	1
2	2	2	2
3	3	3	3
4	4	4	4
5	5	5	5
6	6	6	6
7	7	7	7
8	8	8	8

This classification depends upon the human nose, but it has been put to practical use and has worked remarkably well. For example, 6423 equals Rose. If you call up a dealer in aromatics and say, "Send me four gallons of 6423," you will get shipped to you four gallons of a rose-smelling material.

Dr. John E. Amoore, in his stereochemical theory of odor, suggests that there are seven primary odors, based on the geometry of the molecule of the odorous substance, or *odorant*. Each molecule, because of its size and shape, fits into one appropriately shaped receptor at the olfactory nerve endings in the nose.

The seven primary odors, according to this theory, are: (1) camphoraceous, (2) musky (like angelica root oil), (3) floral, (4) pepperminty, (5) ethereal (like dry-cleaning fluid), (6) pungent (like strong vinegar), and (7) putrid (like a rotten egg). Each of the first five has its own corresponding specially sized and shaped receptors to receive the appropriate molecules. The last two owe their smell not to definite shape-matching in the receptors, but rather to the electric charge of the molecules. The pungent smelling molecules have a positive charge (electrophilic) and the putrid smelling molecules have a negative charge (nucleophilic). So, with the Amoore system, we take the formula of a compound, construct a molecular model of it, measure it, and see into what slot it will fit.

The difficulty of classifying odors is shown by the large number of investigators in the past who have tried their hand at the game. The names of three men are usually mentioned as early classifiers: Rimmel, Zwaardemaker, and Henning.

Rimmel lists eighteen classes of smells.

CLASS	EXAMPLES
1. Rose	Rose, geranium, sweetbrier
2. Jasmine	Jasmine, lily of the valley
3. Orange Blossom	Orange flowers, syringa
4. Tuberose	Tuberose, narcissus, hyacinth
5. Violet	Violet, orrisroot, mignonette
6. Balsamic	Vanilla, heliotrope, tonka beans, balsams of Peru and Tolu
7. Spice	Cinnamon, mace, nutmeg
8. Clove	Clove, carnation
9. Camphor	Camphor, patchouli, rosemary
10. Sandal	Sandalwood, vetiver, cedarwood
11. Citrine	Lemon, orange, bergamot
12. Lavender	Lavender, thyme, marjoram
13. Mint	Peppermint, spearmint, rue, sage
14. Aniseed	Anise seed, caraway, coriander, dill, fennel
15. Almond	Bitter almonds, peach kernels, laurel
16. Musk	Musk, civet
17. Ambergris	Ambergris, oak moss
18. Fruit	Pear, apple, pineapple, quince

This was a cumbersome system. It emphasized the floral and fruity odors but did not find a place for the foul, putrid, and pungent odors that make up a large percentage of the olfactory contacts of daily life.

Zwaardmaker cut the number of classified odors down to nine.

CLASS	EXAMPLES
1. Ethereal	Fruits, beeswax, ethers
2. Aromatic	Camphor, cloves, lavender, lemon, bitter almonds
3. Balsamic or Fragrant	Flowers, violet, vanilla
4. Ambrosial	Amber, musk
5. Alliaceous	Hydrogen sulfide, chlorine, arsine
6. Empyreumatic	Roasted coffee, benzene
7. Caprylic	Cheese, rancid fat
8. Repulsive	Bedbug, deadly nightshade
9. Nauseating or Fetid	Feces, carrion

Henning attempted to simplify the classification still more and offered this modified list of common odors.

CLASS	EXAMPLES
1. Spicy	Cloves, anise, fennel
2. Flowery	Heliotrope, geranium
3. Fruity	Orange, bergamot, citronella
4. Resinous or Balsamic	Turpentine, oil of eucalyptus
5. Burnt	Tar, pyridine
6. Foul	Hydrogen sulfide, carbon disulfide

No perfect classification of odors has as yet been advanced. At least, these men did accomplish a sorting of the many odors they encountered. And to an elephant, none of these class names can describe the smell of a camel.

3!
The Smell of Food and Beverages

OF ALL THE APPETITES, the one that lasts the longest is the appetite for food and drink. You form the habit of eating three times a day when you are young and the habit persists up to your intravenous feeding under Medicare. The noon whistle blows and you drop everything to munch your lunch. At eventide (this is poetic) when you return to your domicile, you expect the evening repast to be awaiting. You consume TV snacks so continually, you can't even find time to brush your teeth between them as you are so frequently warned to do. Some of you who "get up nights" can't walk a straight line but must make a detour via the kitchen to again eat, eat, eat.

Food is a form of matter that has a continual universal appeal. Some yield to this appeal more continually than necessary, and have figures to prove it.

Food is appealing and is enjoyed because of its flavor. You might think this has little to do with smell, but the two are so intimately connected that without the one, you could not have the other. A cultivated sense of smell makes a gourmet out of an ordinary eater. Flavor is the result of the combination or association of taste, smell, texture, and temperature of food. All these sensations artistically fused make an average meal a delight.

Most of you are familiar with the term "taste buds," those nerve endings on the tongue that send a message to the brain to identify the taste of substances placed in the mouth. Some people commonly think that there are only four kinds of taste. This is not exactly true. We can distinguish savory difference in various degrees and combinations of these four basics.

Salt, sour, sweet, bitter—these are the four kinds of taste buds. Each kind is concentrated in a different area, such as the tip, sides, and base of the tongue; and each area possesses many individual taste buds. A child has more sweet taste buds than he will have as an adult and therefore likes sweets. He suffers bruises, insults, humiliations, and other discomforts because of this. In other words, his parents chastise him for having a greater appreciation of sweets than they do.

All you husbands who complain because your wife doesn't flavor her cooking as well as mother did, please note: Your taste buds have altered and diminished since you were "mama's boy."

Recently I visited a relative whom I had not seen since I was a boy. Trying to please me, she prepared what had always been my favorite pie when I had been a youthful guest in her home. The very thought of it was making me drool, because I could vividly recall how I used to enjoy her culinary talent.

How disappointed I was on taking the first bite. Obviously, it was prepared in the identical way, but now it was so sweet, it was sickening. How did I ever think it was so good? The ingredients weren't changed, but with fewer sweet taste buds, my ability to appreciate the pie had altered physically.

In addition to the function of the taste buds, smell adds greatly to food flavor. You smell externally through the nose (by sniffing), and internally through the mouth. When you put food in your mouth and clamp down with your jaws, you force the air of the mouth over the food and up the back stairs of the nasal passage to the olfactory chamber to get the smell in reverse.

Under normal conditions, while eating properly, you are smelling the food both externally and internally. When you get a cold in the head, one of those drippy colds with a lot of mucus covering the inside of the nostrils, food doesn't taste good because you cannot appreciate the aroma. The flavor is lost. Ham will taste like lamb; minced apple like minced onion. Your postnasal drip has cut off the smell sensation inside your mouth.

Sensory end-organs in your nose respond to exceedingly small particles of the odoriferous substances. The amount of a chemical compound that causes the smell of onions, and therefore their flavor, is not only very small but also very elusive. The tantilizing odor of broiling steak is likewise caused by extremely small particles, and they, too, are very fleeting. They'll get away from you if you're not careful.

If food is steamed a lot, the odor is gone with the wind. Some cooks place many pots on the stove while they go on to other chores. Vaporization takes the minute particles of odoriferous substances out of the food, causing them to be lost forever. The steam table of a restaurant is the killer of flavor. Nothing from it resembles the taste of meats or vegetables cooked quickly and served quickly. It is better to cook in covered utensils with less water. Then the particles cannot easily escape; they are trapped within the food.

Overcooking can be ruinous too. Corn on the cob needs only three minutes of steaming for maximum goodness. After that, you'll have the flavor of the cob and not of the corn. Spinach, if you must eat it, does not even have to be submerged in water. Whatever moisture remains on the leaves after washing is sufficient. Simply place it in a closed container over a low flame and heat for fifteen to twenty minutes. Peas need only a few minutes cooking in a small amount of water. The flavor of seafood is spoiled by prolonged cooking.

In certain sections of the country green beans, cabbage, and "greens"—which include such things as turnip and beet tops, mustard greens, and collards—are cooked all day in a large pot of water with ham or salted pork fat. They claim the lengthy boiling prevents your getting "green poisoning." This is not so. There is nothing harmful in greens, even in the raw state.

Anyone can learn to cook something until it is done, but control of evanescent odors by the creative chef is what gives him the touch of an artist, just as subtle coloring can make a picture a masterpiece.

Consider the idea of freshness! You say you like things fresh. What do you mean by freshness? One definition is that a thing is fresh when it has suffered a minimum loss of water. If things are dried out, they're no longer fresh. You know that yourself. They're old and wrinkled like a prune, the only thing acceptable in that state. A food that has sufficient water in it is considered fresh. A newly pulled onion or scallion has freshness because it has water. The plant has not yet dried out.

Freshness also means that there has been a minimum loss of the smelly things called *odoriphores*. These are the tiny bits of matter that give the strawberry its smell; and they gradually disappear with time and temperature. They are sometimes called flavor oils. As a group, they are relatively volatile. They may evaporate quickly. In order to entrap flavors in dry mixes such as dessert powders and cake mixes, one or more vegetable gum additives are used to surround and protect the stability of the "flavor oils." When the pre-prepared food is cooked in water, the gum dissolves. It has no taste and does not affect the digestive tract.

Did you know that you should keep ground coffee in the refrigerator? When you pry off the lid of a vacuum-packed can, you get a powerful, pleasing odor. There is no smell quite like it. Unfortunately, the ambrosia of coffee quickly escapes, and soon it retains little of its original aromaticity. But in a refrigerator it will be so cold that the speed of dispersion of the volatile odoriphores will be slowed down and they will not vaporize so rapidly. Refrigerators should be made with a special receptacle for this purpose.

You can prolong many delightful scents by keeping the product cool. My wife believes what I say, so she tells me.

She suggested keeping my pipe tobacco in the refrigerator for the same reason she stores coffee there. It worked! Who knows, maybe someday, if we keep storing additional oddities, I'll be forced to buy an extra refrigerator just to keep our food.

The third part of the flavor-complex is the texture of food. It has to feel right on the tongue. If I took a spoonful of mashed potatoes that felt like carpet tacks, I'd think something was wrong with the potatoes, or with the wife who prepared the food. And I'd be right to feel so. We want certain foods to be smooth, others rough. Strawberries, for example, should have the roughness of strawberry seeds. Makers of strawberry ice cream could sprinkle strawberry or similar seeds into the mix to give a seedy texture on the tongue. I like to eat raspberries and get the seeds between my teeth, because when I'm sitting comfortably in the evening, I can get one of the seeds out again, bite on it, and get some of the aromatic juice out of it. That's the texture side of seedy berries. In the Philadelphia area, no vanilla ice cream is acceptable without little, rough, black specks of the ground vanilla bean in evidence.

Some years ago, meat packers pumped water into hams to make them weigh more. They had found a good way to sell ham by the pound (of water); water is cheaper than ham, so they pumped it into the product until it became nice and big and heavy. But many customers complained of the rubbery texture and refused to buy such "inflated" hams. The whole flavor of the ham was lost. The water content of ham is now regulated by the Federal Government. If it contains any water in addition to the brine in which it was cured, the label must read, "Water Added." If there is more than ten per cent water, the label must say, "Imitation Ham."

When eggplants begin to wrinkle because of loss of moisture, merchants have been known to submerge them in a tub of water for a while to restore their round plumpness. They will weigh more too.

Sound also plays an important role. You like to hear certain foods. The crispness of potato chips, the brittleness of peanut candy. Restaurateurs claim, "To sell the steak, sell the sizzle."

Can you imagine silent celery? If you bit into some that didn't make a noise, that would be terrifying. Here is the only opportunity some husbands have of being heard in their own home. Pity poor, heckled husbands, who have to keep silent most of the time, even being ordered to "Keep quiet with your celery." Suppose, in addition to this, that a grower cultivated a celery that had a rubbery texture. It would lose most of its flavor and appeal. Rhubarb, horseradish, and hot peppers are expected to have characteristic textures too.

You enjoy some foods hot; others, like beer, cold. Did you ever drink hot beer? It is not drinkable. I was once invited out to a home where the host said that his refrigerator had broken down and the only beer he had was warm. I tried to drink some. It was terrible. Still, they tell me that in merry old England they prefer their beer and scotch at room temperature. Since few homes have central heating there, room temperature may be sixty degrees. American tourists in the British Isles and nearby countries complain of the absence of ice in drinking water and sodas.

Knowing how we appreciate beer for its coldness, I once froze some on a stick like a popsicle to see what would happen. I called it Erb's Beersicle. My results were disappointing but might be improved through research processing. Marketing this on a commercial basis might run into a lot of complications. Each state has its own liquor licensing rules concerning the minimum and maximum alcoholic content of a consumable product. In some localities the retailer would have to have a liquor license to sell it, in some, it might only be sold at a State Liquor Store, while in some areas it would be forbidden entirely.

In the western part of our country one manufacturer does have "martinisicles" on the market. In European countries candy lozenges containing liquor and wine are sold everywhere.

Eye appeal is another factor, especially the color. Brains and liver, as food, have no eye appeal to me, because they don't look like meat. Grape jelly must look purple. If you have mint gumdrops or creme de menthe, you enjoy seeing a green color. You've never seen a purple cow, and purple milk would be revolting. (I believe, however, that "purple cows"—grape-flavored milkshakes—sell well in some places.) Pickles, to be flavorable, must be green.

The word *delicatessen,* taken from German, means "delicate eating." In a Jewish delicatessen, color in food is important. Borscht (beet soup) must be pink. Made from white beets it might taste the same, but it would never sell. Lox (smoked salmon) must be an orange-red. Though spicy odors play a big part in making the cold meats more savory, they have to have their characteristic coloring to improve the flavor.

Many cooks put red and green chopped peppers into a salad to make it more attractive. Chopped red cabbage and radishes do the same thing. Though they may not make the salad taste much different, they make it look prettier and add mystery to the flavor. When you buy pickled cabbage and chowchow such as the Pennsylvania Dutch concoct, you see yellow, green, and red peppers. And nowhere but on the Pennsylvania Dutch tables will you find magenta-colored hard-boiled eggs, which have been so colored by being pickled in red beet juice. The pickle adds unusual flavor to the eggs, and the color heightens the eye appeal.

Chemists have found that if you want to make food taste a little better, you can accentuate its flavor by using nitrogen. Nitrogen is an odorless, tasteless element by itself. Combined with other elements, it forms many compounds such as piperine in pepper, caffeine in coffee, amino acids in protein, and the much publicized monosodium glutamate. The latter is a salt used to bring out the flavor of foods and is sold under various trade names. If you add a little of a nitrogenous compound to your food, it improves the smell and taste and therefore the flavor.

Caffeine, a nitrogen-containing compound, is best known because it gives coffee a certain amount of its taste, though it is often more highly concentrated in other beverages. Actually, it accentuates the taste that is already there.

We can take advantage of the nitrogenous compounds in many ways. When you eat apple pie and put a blop of cheese on top of it, it is as pleasing as finding an out-of-order parking meter. The cheese and apple pie are gustatory associates because the taste and smell of the apples is improved by the nitrogen-containing proteins in the cheese. Milk with apple pie accomplishes the same flavor improvement.

German beer drinkers usually munch on black radishes while drinking. The smell and taste of the brew is given a lift by the nitrogen of the radishes.

A martini without an olive is like ham without an egg. The olive is the nitrogenous portion. You drop in the olive, and you may also want a few extras on the table. In a manhattan, you substitute a cherry for the olive, the nitrogenous adjunct. It might be a delightful change to put the olive in the manhattan and the cherry in the martini. After a few of either, or both, you couldn't tell an olive from a cherry.

Change in food combinations does something. When eating a hamburger, I startled my friends by putting apple butter on it instead of catsup. Although they ridiculed me for doing such an outlandish thing, I liked the flavor. I was nitrogenating the apple butter with the hamburger.

Why do nuts taste much better when they are roasted? Studies have been made to answer this question. Ordinary nuts contain three basic nutrients—fat (or oil), carbohydrate, and protein. The protein is the nitrogenous component.

Let us see what happens when you heat each of these three nutrients. An oil or fat breaks down into glycerol (glycerine) and a fatty acid. These fatty acids do not taste exceptionally good. Since heating the fats of nuts does not improve their taste, you can rule out this constituent as the origin of better flavor.

The carbohydrates are the starches and sugars in the nuts. When you heat carbohydrates, you convert some of them into caramel and simpler sugars. This increases or contributes somewhat to the flavor of the toasted or roasted nuts.

But the proteins—ah, the nitrogenous compounds of the nuts—when these are heated, they break down into less complex nitrogen compounds known as proteoses, peptones, and peptides. And these are the compounds that really make that nut of yours taste better after roasting.

You get the same effect to a certain degree when you toast bread. It's the proteins, the nitrogenous constituents in the bread, that make the toasted slice so flavorful. Many people don't know how to toast the staff of life. They burn it up, which may be good for them, at that. Charcoal (you smokers know about the activated kind) might absorb gases in and below the stomach, producing a slight therapeutic effect. For eye appeal, toast is better when just golden brown, but it is the heating of the protein that gives the better flavor.

The tantalizing aroma of a bakery is one of the most irresistible odors in the world. When I pass one, I compulsively stop to sniff. The smell is free. No politician has levied a tax on that—yet. Even the smell of a chocolate cake in the oven can drive me out of my mind (a short drive). To smell a sponge cake, baked as only the Jewish housewife can prepare it, is a mouth-watering experience.

Some bakeries actually have a fan blowing the aroma right out to the sidewalk. A sneaky way to make an extra buck! Cars stop, people stop, everything stops to inhale a bit of heaven. Newly made loaves smell much more potent and tempting than stale ones; in fact, when stale, they may reek of mold or mildew. Commercially, certain additives are used to prevent or slow down this type of spoilage.

Large establishments have methods for baking quickly, so the bread won't lose as much of the precious aroma as it does in slower home baking. Everything is done to prevent the loss of the odoriphores and moisture. Modern plastic wrapping seals in and traps the aroma as well as the fresh texture for a much longer period of time.

Certain organic chemicals smell exactly like fresh bread. These chemicals, put up in bottle form, are called "bottled loaf" and "liquid bread." By resorting to the use of these preparations on the wrappings and in the printing inks used on the labels, the bakers can make the wrapped loaves keep their air of newness and freshness indefinitely.

You've heard the old statement, "It sells like hot cakes."

Hot cakes capitalize on their aroma. They permeate the air with a terrific fragrance. In my youth, one of my biggest thrills was the annual visit to the county fair, where the atmosphere was ornate and mystifying. The colorful exhibits, the parachute jumper from a large balloon, and the games of chance were fascinating, but the eating concessions were the places that were really captivating. One such stand gave out free samples of hot cakes to encourage further purchases. The owners knew no one could stop with just one "flannel cake," as we called them then, and eventually you would buy their packaged ready-mixed flour.

As you might guess, I stood in line many, many times because I had more time than money. Even if I got lost, which was easy in the huge crowd, I could always smell my way back to the flannel-cake stand.

And of course the smell of hot cakes is delightful at breakfast time. You husbands who are very early risers can hasten the awakening of the rest of the family by placing a small amount of diluted furfural on a fan or the air conditioner, thereby filling the house with the delicious odor of hot cakes.

On Shrove Tuesday, the Pennsylvania Dutch make raised doughnuts, square or rectangular in shape, to be eaten before Fastnacht or Fawsnacht (Fast Night). When this intoxicating odor fills the home, you know that Lent is at hand. My mother used to make doughnuts the previous evening, allowing the potato dough to rise in a crock overnight near the warm kitchen stove. In the morning, before I arose, she began frying them in deep fat, and the telltale vapors spread as fast as a cold virus in a classroom. You can bet this soon made me get up, because the last one out of bed that day was called a "Fastnacht" and was a target for ridicule the rest of the day. Before the doughnuts were cool, I began snitching them every time my mother's back was turned, and I always wound up with a pre-Lenten bellyache.

Other religious holiday customs are highlighted by foods that depend on nitrogenous ingredients for their flavor. During the Jewish festival of the Passover, the roasted lamb bone and egg represent the burnt offerings. A paste of apples, nuts, and spices signifies the mortar used in the Jews' heavy toil as slaves, and horseradish, substituting for bitter herbs, represents the bitterness of life under the Egyptians. How delightful is the wine they serve with a nut in each glass! Nuts have also become an integral part of our New Year celebrations, for nuts are an age-old symbol of bounty in connection with the new year. Every section of the country has its own favorite nitrogenous dish at this time. In one section, sauerkraut with pork is a must the first day of the year. In another, black-eyed peas mark the day.

Most holiday feasts stress the traditional meats associated with the season. The Polish introduced the custom of eating ham at Easter. The Jews used eggs with their Passover long before Christians incorporated them into Easter observances. Once, turkey roasting in the oven could only mean Thanksgiving Day was here. Thanks to modern scientific methods of raising turkeys and the use of refrigerated trains and planes for quick transportation, they are now plentiful the entire year.

You may think that selling something sweet would not be a hard job, but when you're in the business of candy manufacturing, you still have to compete with other sweet-smelling, sweet-tasting, edible products.

The smell of fudge! Home-made ambrosia! It does something in your home. And all chocolate confections are simply captivating because of their indescribable smell and taste. They contain some essence that has not yet been fully isolated. If you can synthesize an artificial taste or flavoring that is truly like chocolate, you will become rich enough to embrace instant retirement. Substances that smell like chocolate have been found, but the real chocolate taste made artificially still resists discovery. But try stirring a spoonful of instant coffee and a few drops of vanilla extract into a glass of milk. You may also wish to add sugar or some other sweetener. The resulting drink will have the taste of chocolate milk if the ingredients are unknown to the drinker. The nearest "fake" to the imitation chocolate problem!

You young men who present the current "light of your life" with a gift box of delicious chocolate-veneered morsels will experience a thrill from the overpowering vapors escaping from the container. You're in imminent danger of consuming more than she does.

Knowing what this can do to a person, a well-known manufacturer of sweets suggests purchasing two boxes at a time—"one to give, and one to give in to."

Carnivals are notorious for their wild mixture of olfactory sensations. All their odors together clash. Yet the one that has the brute strength to make itself known above all the others is the odor from the "cotton candy" or "cotton floss" stand. This little 6-by-8-foot retailer of nonsense has the highest broadcasting frequency anywhere around. If you can pass it by, your age is showing. The cloudlike product attached to a paper cone appears monstrous and economical, but it doesn't weigh much. If you pushed it together, you'd get only a little blob of sticky sugar. They fluff it up much like girls tease their hair. It is nothing but a little bit of sugar, not hair, teased way out of proportion; but the smell—ah, it's crippling. Coloring matter is sometimes added for visual attraction, as if you needed any other stimulant.

Candy can also be improved by nitrogen compounds. That's why bars with nuts are tastier and more sought after than nutless candy bars. Without them, you might as well munch on a lump of sugar, which is cheaper.

Next to our love for the odor of bakery products and confections, we all thoroughly savor the smell of cooking meat. We hear a great deal about the substances called meat tenderizers. Now, what have these to do with smell? Meat smells better while it is being partially digested, or just before it is completely digested. That is why you heat meat—to partially digest it. You boil it, you roast it, and you stew it to bring out the hidden flavor. A raw steak doesn't smell as good as one that has been grilled over an open fire. In fact, raw steak may stink, especially if it is not too fresh.

So what does a meat tenderizer do? First, it begins to digest the meat. The most popular tenderizer comes from the papaya, a tropical American tree. Inside the fruit of this tree is a substance called an enzyme. An enzyme is an organic catalyst, or helper, that increases the speed of any type of chemical or physiological reaction. Its mere presence does the trick. In the papaya juice there is a specific enzyme known as papain that speeds up the digestion of protein. When it comes in contact with the meat, it breaks down or digests the meat proteins into simpler proteoses, peptones, and peptides, which smell and taste better than the raw meat.

As the meat tenderizer breaks down the proteins, it also makes it possible for the odoriphores to be more readily released. And it improves the texture, making the meat tender so that you can chew it, even if you have bad uppers and worse lowers, because its fibers are digested and broken apart. Tenderizers are never harmful, even if used in excess.

If I had put some gastric juice, the digestive fluid from the stomach, on the meat, the protein would start the same change. The gastric juice contains a digestive enzyme known as pepsin, which does the same thing as the papain of the meat tenderizer does outside the stomach.

Some butchers apply tenderizers to their cheaper cuts of steak before putting them on display in refrigerated show cases. There is nothing harmful in this, but it is useless, because the papain will not function much below room temperature. Other butchers disapprove of this practice because they are proud of the natural quality of their meats. They feel that the use of tenderizers would be an unfavorable reflection on their products.

If you don't want to buy a meat tenderizer as such, you can make your own with ordinary canned or fresh pineapple juice, which has another enzyme called bromelin. This does exactly the same thing as pepsin in the stomach or papain in papaya. Drinking pineapple juice with your meal helps to digest meat by supplementing the pepsin of the gastric juice, which is frequently overworked by excessive indulgence. Your pepsin will take off its hat to the pineapple juice if it prevents your stomach from feeling a little queasy. Remember this when on your vacation. Traveling our national highways to see more of God's country, you may make the mistake of patronizing ulcer-trap diners and road stands where steaks have been marinated in liquid latex before they are fried to a golden-brown in axle grease. Once the order is placed before you, it's embarrassing to retreat. Just ask for a large glass of pineapple juice and have faith in your digestive powers.

Now that your meat is ready to cook, spices will add pizzazz. They are often used to give otherwise common or flavorless dishes more interest gastronomically. When a man reaches for the ketchup or catsup bottle, you can rest assured he doesn't like the original flavor. That is why so much ketchup is splashed on everything called food served at highway "eat joints." If the taste were pleasing, why would anything have to be added? Ketchup is summertime's counterirritant.

Spices are any of various pungent, aromatic vegetable products that mingle with foods readily and impart their basic taste and smell to everything with which they come in contact. They include cloves, allspice, cinnamon, mace, etc. Herbs are plants that do not produce woody tissue and are also appreciated for their aromatic addition to food preparation. Some typical herbs are mint, sage, and basil.

Our choice of spices may depend on what part of the world was our place of origin. The favorite in India is curry. People from Mediterranean countries enjoy oregano, basil, and hot peppers. Europeans like cloves, allspice, and mustard. This does not mean, of course, that we are limited to just the spices mentioned; anyone may utilize any or all of the variety available in today's market. Creative cooks are always looking for something exotic to prepare.

Before man knew how to make ice, either mechanically or electrically, most of the meat he ate was preserved by being cured in brine, smoked, or dried. Chances are that any raw meat was slightly tainted before reaching the table, so to disguise the spoilage and the fetid odor, spices were used as a cover-up. Perhaps the elephant would even like a clove-scented camel!

Since spices were expensive, because they had to be imported from the Orient, the mistress of the house always kept them locked in a special cabinet. It was customary for her to wear a little pouch for the key, attached to the belt of her dress. She never trusted anyone.

We still pickle, dry, and smoke meats. All of you are impressed with the fragrance of wood. Have you ever driven past a sawmill on some scenic tour without slowing down just a mite to take a lingering sniff? When wood is burning, the vaporizing of its essential oils fills our hearts with nostalgia, be it for a hearth on a chilly evening or a mirth-filled cookout in the summer.

Most popular of all is the effect that hickory smoke has on meat. Even if you have more smoke in your eyes than on the rotisserie, it is a necessary part of preparing an outdoor feast. Though restaurants may proudly advertise their hickory-grilled steaks by a neon sign, it is possible that they never use one splinter of hickory wood, or old matchsticks, or any kind of wood. They can get the flavor in a bottle— "liquid smoke." You can purchase it at the local supermarket for your own use, even if you only plan to fry your steak in the usual way in your kitchen.

The "essential oils" of wood and all vegetation are not really oils in the strictest sense; they are not true fats. Chemists didn't know what else to call them. They only knew that, besides being essential to the plants that produce them, they act like oils, they pour like oils, and many are oily or greasy looking. Most of them are clear. They give to the plants their characteristic smell and taste, and can be extracted in several ways.

Essential oils are found throughout the plants—in blossoms, leaves, fruit, roots, etc. They consist of a mixture of many organic chemical compounds, some of which are called esters. The smell of flowers and fruit is characterized by their esters or compounds formed when an alcohol and an organic acid unite in the bonds of chemistry.

One such ester is methyl salicylate, found in oil of wintergreen, which is used to give a sweet-minty flavor to confections. Among the thousands of other esters are ethyl butyrate in pineapples, octyl acetate in oranges, amyl salicylate in clover, amyl butyrate in apricots, and benzyl acetate in jasmine. Knowing the composition of esters, man has been able to reproduce many of them synthetically. Natural strawberry flavoring would be in short supply since there are not enough strawberries grown to provide all the strawberry flavoring demanded. Synthetic strawberry esters must fill the need.

If I pick a rose, for example, and distill it, I get the essential oil of rose. If I distill cloves, I get oil of cloves. Oil of coffee and oil of tea can be extracted similarly, which is lucky. Imagine the confusion if one got oil of peppermint instead. If I distill catnip leaves, I get something to make the feline world go ga-ga. It makes even big cats like lions and tigers quite playful. If you ever go to Africa, carry a spray gun filled with oil of catnip. If, by chance, a lion comes toward you, it might help to spray him liberally. He could die laughing. Even if oil of catnip is an essential oil, we seldom use it. It makes a purr-r-r-fect tea when brewed from the herb, but it might attract all the tabbies in the neighborhood.

And now, to a purely American topic—the hot dog and the hamburger. No respectable highway would be without a stand selling them. A plane from India, scheduled to land in New York City, was forced by fog to land in the northern part of the State. Several of the passengers who were very anxious to get to Albany were told they would be taken there by way of Buffalo. In the meantime, they were welcome to partake of refreshments at the hot-dog stand. One gentleman from India was shocked. He thought the United States was too advanced to make people ride on buffaloes and eat dog meat.

The enterprising operator of a roadside stand should take a lesson from the bakery. Blow, blow, blow the odoriferous vapors out into the atmosphere with a strong fan. He could snare the passer-by with an irresistible force. Big lighted signs may attract the traveler's eye, but it would be more effective to pull him in by the nose.

There are two ways of preparing hot dogs: One is to throw them into steaming hot water to boil them and to sterilize them. But in this method the odoriphores are lost in the steam, which is soon dissipated. When you grill them, on the other hand, you're actually toasting them like nuts. The protein in the hot dogs or hamburger is nitrogenous, and is being changed to proteoses, etc., as in digestion. These derived proteins give the meat a pleasant, long-lasting, attractive flavor. An open grill or hot plate with meat frying and sizzling is a great attention-getter. Often the vapor that is wafted out is better than the taste. A wise chef also includes a hot toasted roll to enhance the flavor of the meat.

Sometimes it is hard to determine just what kind of meat goes into the making of a hamburger. It should consist of ground beef, but remember that one definition of beef is simply "muscular flesh." So, what's a hamburger?

A law has been passed in Pennsylvania saying that the sale of kangaroo meat is unlawful in the state. Up until the time the law was passed, I didn't know kangaroo meat was ever used. Now it's illegal, indicating that some of those roadside stands might have sold hopping good hamburgers that contained anything swallowable. When you are traveling in strange territory at lunch time, it's so convenient to pull into a drive-in for a quick snack. If you get a fairly decent smell from it and you're hungry enough, you'll eat anything for a relatively high cost, including dry, rubbery buns and the usual withered trimmings.

Besides having questionable meat content, hamburgers sometimes are adulterated with fillers such as bread crumbs, but as long as there is enough meat to impart the proper flavor, the eater may be none the wiser. Some stands are very generous; others economize by weighing each hamburger, which was previously formed within a little ring. One short-order cook bragged he made thirty hamburgers from a pound of ground meat.

Elephants would not stop at a stand selling camel-burgers!

With or without? That's the next question. Onions? Mustard? Both contain an element named sulfur, which is a yellow, solid material. Combined with oxygen (or air) it makes a choking, poisonous gas called sulfur dioxide. Sulfur compounds are in the essential oils of onions, mustard, garlic, turnips, radishes, and the cabbage family. They produce sharp, harsh, pungent flavors. The oils of onion and garlic have been isolated, making it commercially possible to market them in bottles. There is a new liquid garlic extract which retains all the flavor but none of the odor. Its slogan is, "Breath Takes a Holiday."

Every year, on a fine summer's day, thousands of Pennsylvanians knowingly sniff the air and confidently follow their noses. The scent leads them straight to Long Park, an idyllic spot of green at the edge of Lancaster and the scene of the world's biggest chicken barbecue. It is sponsored by Lancaster's Sertoma Club and is a dawn-to-dusk outdoor event. While Sertoma members and their families keep the barbecue fires burning, nearly 17,000 chicken fanciers converge on the park, consume more than 14,000 chicken halves, tons of coleslaw, and gallons of ice cream, coffee, and soft drinks.

The smell of popcorn, a long-time favorite, is one of the first odors that hits you when you go into a motion-picture theater today. The olfactory appeal of popcorn causes many people to stock up before they get situated. Some movies have refreshment breaks when time-out is given for re-charging the popcorn boxes. Other people find the smell of popcorn unpleasant, especially when too concentrated. That may be one of the reasons for the popularity of the outdoor drive-in theater—but only one of the reasons.

Butter and salt go hand-in-hand with the popcorn. Salt has a tendency to bring out the flavor of any food, and many people use it for just that purpose. Salty potato chips are a popular noisy snack, and my wife even claims that salt emphasizes the odor and taste of watermelon. I am the opposite: I eat sugar on my celery.

In our modern economy, dairying is a major industry. Americans have been mass-educated to believe that milk is necessary as a food. Still, we are the only weaned adults who continue to drink milk. It is convenient to drink and you may enjoy the taste, but many must pass it quickly under their noses without sniffing, so that its bovine smell will not produce nausea. Some people flavor it with choco-late or malt or egg-nog to mask the milky, animal, hircine stink. The reek of sour milk is caused by a small amount of butyric acid, a fatty acid also present in sweat. Food fed to cows also influences the odor of milk. A compound called diacetyl, a derivative of the acid that gives vinegar its sour-ness, is responsible for the characteristic odor of butter. It is also found in cheese, as well as in certain non-dairy products.

Cheese depends on the stink it produces. The very thing you denounce in a rotten egg is the quality you demand in certain types of cheese, such as limburger. The moldier it is, the more you smack your beer-moistened lips over it. It contains nitrogen, and it doesn't upset your stomach.

Many dairy products are the result of bacteria acting on milk. Bacteria can cause a lot of changes besides making you sick. Most of them are beneficial. Manufacturers are even using bacterial action to convert ordinary petroleum into synthetic protein for underdeveloped countries. Unfortunately, they find that the protein so produced lacks the customary smells and tastes with which Mother Nature has so generously endowed her own protein products. Chemicals or synthetic odorants have to be added to make it acceptable even to very hungry people.

We commonly eat with such haste that we need liquids to wash down our partially chewed food. A few bites, a gulp of beverage—this is the speedy way of making the most of the lunch hour. Coffee is undoubtedly the most common flavored beverage. It not only is consumed at practically every meal but is the reason given for time-out from work, the popular coffee break. Instant coffee is the outcome of our quest for speed. Dried, powdered, instant coffee and tea have lost much of their original odor and taste. The fact is that no instant coffee has as yet captured the real aroma of the freshly infused preparation. Tea owes its flavor largely to the volatile oil of tea. It has been extracted and has an intense penetrating odor. Cinnamon and rum are used in combination with tea in Germany. Spain prefers the lemon-verbena odor with hers.

In discussions of alcoholic beverages, the word "bouquet" frequently comes into play. Do you drink booze because you want to obtain the feeling of being drunk, or do you really enjoy the subtle aroma from the various wines, rums, whiskies, brandies, and liqueurs? The pleasant bouquets emanating from wines and from brandies (which are distilled wines) are due largely to esters from the grape or other wine-making fruit. The odor and taste of the alcohol in the beverages of low concentration is feeble.

The bouquet of brandy can best be appreciated if it is imbibed properly. To experience the delicate aroma, brandy should be drunk slowly, ever so slowly, from convex glasses called snifters. The warmth of the cupped hands vaporizes the esters, which are then partially confined in the brandy glass for inhaling and enjoyment.

Nonalcoholic drinks are also flavored with esters—but when the esters are dissolved in alcohol, the pleasantness of the odor is enhanced.

The aging of wines and other alcoholic beverages is important. When the beverages are first fermented, other alcohols besides grain or ethyl alcohol are formed. These other alcohols have a somewhat disagreeable odor. They are more toxic too. During the aging process, these "rotten" alcohols are slowly converted into less harmful and even more delightful aromatic esters.

I made a bottle of dandelion wine for home consumption. During the bottling, a fly dropped into it, but even with the corpse inside, I stored it away. Now, after about fifteen years, I think I'll scoop out the embalmed fly and serve the wine to my guests while *I* drink coffee. It certainly has aged long enough. I think I'll mount the fly.

Many esters are available to make your own instant liquor —that is if you can obtain the necessary alcohol. For example, the ester ethyl formate dissolved in alcohol makes a good artificial rum. I have made cognac in the same way —for research purposes, naturally.

You must not forget water as a beverage. Because our

potable water is re-used again and again, it is treated chemically with chlorine gas to make it safe from infectious "bugs." Since the streams that are our source of water are being polluted with sewage and industrial waste, the odor and taste is bound to be changed. It is known that when industries dump phenols and phenolic wastes into rivers and water is subsequently chlorinated, it will be offensive to swallow. Coffee, tea, and other beverages made from such chlorinated-phenolic "slop" will seldom make you call for seconds. If you want good water, drink it in the form of beer. Brewers know the secret of getting theirs from a spring.

At Springmill, Pennsylvania, a few miles west of Philadelphia, there is a bubbling spring so pure, it is used by a nationally known paper mill to make the finest, whitest paper in the country. This flawless white paper is used to print the names of the winners for the annual Oscar Awards in Hollywood. Since more than five million gallons of water per day gush forth from the spring, it is too bad the mill does not share the water with a brewery. What beer that could make!

Smells are even being used to fool our animal friends. We have synthetic plastic bones, impregnated with something that tastes and smells like meat. The poor dog sniffs, thinks it is the real bone, and chews on it. When I was discussing this on a radio "participation" program, a listener called in to say that her local newspaper had recently featured a large ad for ham. The ink was red and contained a synthetic odorant so realistic that her dog ate the paper. They also make synthetic cheese for mice, using plastic sponge treated in the same manner. One nice thing, you can use this fake cheese over and over again. The trap may wear away, but the bait is always as good as new. The rat you smell may be a chemist.

4!
The Smell of Society

WEBSTER DEFINES SOCIETY as "a community, a nation, or a broad grouping of people having common traditions, institutions, and collective activities and interests." The grouping may be all male, all female, or mixed. Sometimes people gather for a specific purpose, sometimes for no good reason at all. Since society is a heterogeneous mixture, its smell is heterogeneous too.

No matter how large the assemblage may be, it is always

composed of individuals. Each member is distinguishable by his personal redolence or offensiveness, as a result of his hygienic habits, dietary peculiarities, or exposure to odoriferous particles.

Someone has said, I think it was I, that a bedbug can detect the presence of a man two whole city blocks away, and a woman—well. Our society is well known to the bedbug. Recently the U.S. military establishment has actually put this fact to practical use. They have tested a detection device in Vietnam in which bedbugs are enclosed in a small box coupled to an air-intake that can be directed toward spots where enemy guerrillas may be hiding. Any noises of excitement made by the bugs are electronically amplified and can be heard through earphones worn by the operator!

You can tolerate the fragrance, or lack of it, of one person, but when multiplied by fifty, a hundred, or perhaps thousands, the stench can become unbearable.

Did you ever smell a gym after a class has completed its calisthenics? Then, there is the chlorinated mustiness of indoor pools where large groups of half-naked swimmers are splashing and churning their bodies in an atmosphere of high humidity and low ventilation.

When I proctor an examination in a large room holding say three hundred to four hundred students, the air at the end of several hours smells as if it needs changing, like dirty laundry awaiting washing. It is a fetor that defies classification, but to me it's just plain sickening. I want out!

The smoke-filled rooms of stag parties, political maneuvering, poker sessions, and other hanky-panky are oppressive because of their tinctorial nicotinic smog.

In night clubs, where the tables are placed so close together that the patrons eat from each others' plates, they fan their odors throughout the entire stuffy atmosphere. The exhausted guests of such clubs do not smell to high heaven, but rather to a much lower place.

When mixed society gathers for the purpose of drinking, socially, that is, the sum total of all the concentrated exhaled alcohol-laden air is so strong, it would be dangerous to strike a match.

Bankers tell me that when they open the vaults in the morning, the smell of dirty paper money is unbearable. Paper money, no matter how much you like it, is really filthy lucre. Smell it sometime before you spend it. It is said that some banks actually give the dirty bills an odorizing treatment before sending them on their smelly daily spending spree. Frozen assets would smell much better.

Chemists and other interested artisans must come to the rescue of society to make the world safe for democracy as far as olfaction is concerned. This has always been a social problem, so let's go back in history to see what our ancestors accomplished.

The earliest record of the use of perfume comes from ancient Egypt. After maids had bathed their mistresses, they rubbed olive oil over their bodies to insure smoothness of the skin. In that heat, you can imagine what happened when the oil became rancid. One day a maid said, "I think I'll put some flowers in the oil to see what happens."

The word spread like news of a bargain sale, and a fad was born. Each maid began to experiment with different blossoms in an effort to enhance the bodily attractiveness of her mistress. As the rivalry increased, the variety of fragrances multiplied, giving rise to the perfume industry.

Because nothing was known of fixatives, the pungency of the early perfumes soon dissipated. To overcome this, the Egyptians hid little vials of *perfumari* in the braids of their wigs. Did you think your hairpiece was a modern innovation? Women living along the Nile four thousand years ago made it fashionable to have a different wig for each costume.

They were the first to overcome body odor, but not the only ones. Every primitive society got the word and did likewise.

The Bible contains many references to the use of precious ointments. Remember how Ruth bathed and covered herself with fragrance before going to the threshing floor to entice Boaz? She was no dummy. Women were not alone in their desire to smell attractive. It is written that Alexander the Great soaked his clothing in perfume, and Julius Caesar wasn't opposed to it either. The only time mankind frowned on the use of aromatic toiletries was during the Dark Ages, when perfume was considered an instrument of the devil. No wonder they were called the Dark Ages—everything was so dirty. Those poor souls even convinced themselves that long-standing perspiration was sexy.

In spite of its long history, the production of perfume has been diversified, improved, and increased more in our lifetime than in all the centuries gone by. It is one of the largest industries in the world today. More is being spent by women, or by men for women, for fragrance than for education and religion put together. A woman not interested in perfume is not interesting.

Fragrances are not for females only. The male has always enjoyed good smells, but until recently he applied fragrances to himself only in secret or when the fragrance accompanied substances of apparent practical use, such as after-shave lotions, hair tonics, etc. To get these smells without seeming effeminate, he called upon his barber, who doused him liberally with witch hazel and bay rum. But now, with increasing bravado men are buying perfume openly. "Yours

Forever," "Girl Response," and "For Gentlemen" are names
being used to appeal to the virile sex. The fragrances,
though floral in nature, are hidden behind such descriptions
as woodsy, ferny, mossy, and leathery. Such labels sell better
than lily-of-the-valley or petunia.

How do you get perfume? Well, perfumes can be obtained from plants by a number of different methods. You
can distill the odors from a sweet-smelling plant such as
bergamot or lilac by placing leaves, petals, roots, or other
parts of the plant in an apparatus known as a still. Many of
the stills operate with the aid of steam. The distillate con-
sists of highly odorous oils, the essential oils, which go to
make some of our perfumes.

Another method for extracting these essential oils from
plants is by dissolving the plant oils in fat. We are all familiar with the fact that odoriferous material will adhere to or
be absorbed in fat. You can therefore extract the odor of
roses, gardenias, etc., merely by keeping the petals in contact with solid fat for a time, then chemically separating
the fat from the essential oil. This process is called *enfleur-
age*.

The essential oils may also be obtained by solution or
extraction, i.e., by adding a certain suitable solvent such
as chloroform, ether, or alcohol to the blossoms and agitat-
ing. The solvent dissolves the essential oil, and after the
solvent is permitted to evaporate, the less volatile plant
essence remains.

Another method, with which some of you are familiar,
is the physical action called compression or expression.
It's simply application of pressure. When we press on certain types of plants, the oil squirts right out of them. You
can do this in your own home. You will need peelings from
an orange or lemon or other citrus fruit and a flame such as

a burning candle. Squeeze a piece of the orange peeling, aiming it so that it squirts into the candle flame. You will hear and see a sputtering due to the essential oil of orange hitting the hot flame. You don't have to go out and buy fresh oranges for this home experiment; peelings from the garbage can be used. Orange peels are notorious for their strong smell. As soon as anybody opens his lunch and peels an orange, everybody within inhaling distance knows it.

As a researcher in osmics, essential oils have always fascinated me. You too may be interested in a tabulation of some of the more common essential oils and their uses.

ESSENTIAL OILS	USES
Oil of Angelica	In manufacturing liqueurs, cordials, and gins; in perfumes of the chypre type; in toothpaste, mouth washes, and dentifrices
Oil of Anise	In manufacturing liqueurs, flavor for candies, cookies, dentifrices
Oil of Bay	In bay rum
Oil of Bergamot	In perfumery (base of eaux de Cologne), hair oils, pomades, and for masking disagreeable odors
Oil of Bitter Almonds	In cosmetics, creams, lotions, and perfumes; only the oil free from HCN may be used for liqueurs and foods.
Oil of Bitter Orange	In flavors and perfumes
Oil of Caraway	In liqueurs and perfuming soaps; flavor for cookies, candies

Essential Oils	Uses
Oil of Cardamon	In perfumes and flavors
Oil of Catnip	Used by trappers as an animal lure
Oil of Cedar Leaf	In medicinal preparations, particularly inhalants; as a substitute for oil of lavender
Oil of Cedar Wood	In perfumery; as insect repellents
Oil of Celery	In flavor for soft drinks and unpleasant medicaments
Oil of Cinnamon	In food flavors and perfumes
Oil of Citronella	In perfumes and insectifuges
Oil of Clove	In confectionery and tooth powders
Oil of Coriander	In flavoring; perfumes and soaps
Oil of Eucalyptus	In medicinal preparations, such as cough drops, mouth washes, gargles, inhalants, room sprays, and medicated soaps
Oil of Fennel	In masking unpleasant medicines
Oil of Geranium	In perfumery, as odorant for tooth and dusting powders, ointments, hair tonics, etc.
Oil of Ginger	In mouth washes, ginger beverages, liqueurs, etc.
Oil of Hops	In flavors for soft drinks and dry hopping in breweries
Oil of Juniper	In perfumery, liqueurs (base of gin), flavors
Oil of Lavender	In perfumery and flavors
Oil of Lemon	In flavors for liqueurs, pastry, beverages, and in perfumes

Essential Oils	Uses
Oil of Linaloe	In perfumery
Oil of Marjoram	In perfumes and flavors
Oil of Mustard	In flavors
Oil of Nutmeg	In flavors
Oil of Parsley	In flavors
Oil of Patchouli	In perfumery
Oil of Pepper	In condiments
Oil of Peppermint	In flavoring liqueurs, toothpaste, mouth washes, etc.
Oil of Pettigrain	In perfumes
Oil of Rose	In perfumes, flavoring for lozenges, and toilet preparations
Oil of Rosemary	In liniments and hair lotions
Oil of Sassafras	In flavors, especially the root-beer type
Oil of Turpentine	In solvents
Oil of Verbena	In perfumery
Oil of Wintergreen	In chewing gum, candies, etc.; in medicinal liniments
Oil of Ylang-Ylang	In perfumery

A perfume may be relatively simple in its composition, or it may be quite complex. Perfumes are mixtures and are usually tailored to meet definite needs and specifications. Perfumes not only are used as such but also find their way into the manufacture of many cosmetic preparations such as lipstick, bath salts, hair preparations, soaps, and powders.

A perfume is composed of three basic components: (1) a solvent; (2) an odorous substance (usually several); and (3) a fixative.

It is important that the solvent used have a pleasing smell. Years ago, when ethyl alcohol was used as the solvent, the odorous material sometimes evaporated before the alcohol, and the perfume wearer smelled like a boozer. To reek of warm alcohol, whisky, or rum puts one on a different level of society, "high" society. Today, many members of the social group smell like alcohol when they begin an evening's activities. The liquor camouflages the perfume meant to camouflage the sweat. If the solvent is malodorous, the perfume will be too.

How can you make the scent last long enough so that you will be socially correct all through the night of such affairs? Add chemical substances to prevent the highly volatile portions of the perfume from leaving before you do. Such additives are called fixatives, and the phenomenon is known as a fixation.

Fixation is the process of fixing the various components in a perfume or preventing them from evaporating too rapidly or at an unequal rate. It is a somewhat complicated action, involving a number of chemical and physical factors that are not fully understood. However, the principle of fixation implies that all of the components in a given mixture of liquids have the same evaporation rate or boiling point.

In the better types of perfume the fixative, either odorous or nonodorous, which has a low vapor pressure and therefore a low volatility, is mixed with an odorous substance of high vapor pressure and therefore high volatility. Moncrieff, in *The Chemical Senses,* illustrates the role of a fixative with an experiment using acetone, which is highly volatile because of its high vapor pressure. A quantity of acetone placed on a watch glass in a warm room will evaporate in a few minutes. But if the same quantity of acetone is dissolved in an equal quantity of water and placed on a watch glass in the same warm room, its rate of evaporation will gradually slow down as its concentration in the water decreases, and there will still be some acetone left in the water after a much longer time than it took for the undiluted acetone to evaporate. The water in this case acts as the fixative.

Some of the fixatives used are of animal origin, such as ambergris, castoreum, civet, and musk. New fixatives are being isolated from animals, and musk-like secretions are found in the common muskrat or musquash. A few essential oils are used as fixatives, the more important being clary, orris, patchouli, sage, sandalwood, and vetiver. Resinous fixatives are materials exuded from certain plants, such as the resin benzoin; the gums, myrrh and labdanum; the balsams, Peru, Tolu, copaiba, and storax; the oleoresin terpene; and the resinoid ambrein.

Without fixation you could get into trouble. Some perfumes have as many as thirty or forty different constituents, all of which could evaporate at different rates. By the time an evening was half spent, the aroma would be entirely different from what it had been. Of course, that's when the powder room comes in handy—you can replenish the original redolence. Some powder rooms have little coin boxes on the wall that dispense perfume, so my wife tells me. She overheard a woman warn her companion not to use them, because they attract the wrong kind of men.

The same constituents, in different proportions, make two different perfumes. Here we have a formulation for a rose perfume and a lilac perfume, listed in parts per 200.

		Rose	Lilac
ALDEHYDES:	Hydroxycitronellal	2	30
	Anisic aldehyde	1	10
	Cyclamen aldehyde	1	1

		Rose	Lilac
	Heliotropin	2	15
	Aldehyde C-11	2–10	1
	Phenyl acetic aldehyde 50%	5	3
ALCOHOLS:	Cinnamic alcohol	10	15
	Anisic alcohol	1	10
	Phenyl ethyl alcohol	25	15
	Linalool	3	3
	Terpineol	5	15
	Citronellol	10	1
	Geraniol	35	2
	Phenyl propyl alcohol	1	1
ESTERS:	Benzyl acetate	3	10
	Terpinyl acetate	2	1
KETONES:	Irisone, alpha	7	1
	Musk ketone	10	10
	Benzophenone	5	1
PHENOL:	Isoeugenol	1	5
ACID:	Phenyl acetic acid	1	2–10
LACTONE:	Coumarin	1	1
ACETAL:	Phenyl acetaldehyde dimethyl acetal 5%	2	1
AROMATIC BROMINE COMPOUND:	Bromstyrol	2	1
AROMATIC NITROGEN COMPOUND:	Indole 10%	2	16
ESSENTIAL OILS:	Ylang-Ylang	1	3
	Bergamot	2	1
	Geranium bourbon	8	1–10
PLANT RESINS:	Essence of Styrax	1	5
	Guaiacwood	5	1
	Balsam of Peru 10%	2	2

		Rose	*Lilac*
FLORAL OILS:	Jasmine absolute 10%	5	5
	Oil of rose	2	1–10
ANIMAL			
RESIN:	Civet 3%	10	10
DILUENT:	Diethyl phthalate	25	
		200	200

It is impossible for the average person to distinguish the rose from the lilac preparation. The label is what helps you know the difference. If I put a lilac label on the rose perfume, people will say it smells like lilac. You can fool the public a great deal with insinuating labels. The names of many perfumes suggest that virtue does not make scents.

We've discussed how you endeavor to enhance your physical appeal by putting on something to mask your real self. But perhaps, after spending all that money, you are still not satisfied. In more recent years, we've developed a desire to take certain smells off. Now you are spending even more to deodorize yourself, so there will be no conflict of interests. You frantically seek to eliminate any chance of offending (we all do it at times). Cosmetics commercials stress this. For instance, everyone perspires! This accumulation in certain areas of the body putrefies and makes you more pungent than a clean human being should be. Osmidrosis or bromhidrosis is a condition in which the perspiration has an abnormally strong odor. We term it B.O.

The principal cause of B.O. is the bacterial decomposition of perspiration. Two types of perspiration are known, apocrine and eccrine. The first is believed to be the culprit when germs get with it. We also have sebaceous glands which secrete an oily substance. I have some on my nose right now, making it shiny. Look at your own proboscis.

It's shiny too! When a woman's nose gets shiny, it is immediately covered over with make-up. We poor men are helpless. The sebaceous glands manufacture and secrete the product called sebum. This also can putrefy, become rancid, and cause another kind of body odor.

One can't wash after every meal, you know! How dangerously embarrassing if a person has to go out to a dinner party immediately after working hours with no chance for a shower. Some people don't bathe before the party starts, and some don't or can't bathe even after it's over. Naturally, a good, strong, distinctive odor develops. Etiquette says, "You must try to get rid of this." You will not dance with a girl who repels, nor will she dance with you, if you do. In lieu of taking a bath right at the affair, you substitute chemicals for cleanliness.

There are all sorts of gadgets for applying a deodorant. You can rub it on, you can roll it on, you can spray it on, you can use powders, you can use liquids, you can use creams. The whole idea is simply to mask the abnormal putridity. Sometimes you must use antiperspirants, chemicals that will slow down your rate of perspiring for a certain length of time. These are also applied in the same way— by rolling, rubbing, spraying, or patting with deodorant pads, to avoid the danger of offending.

One thing that is necessary for all cosmetics is fragrance. Maybe grandma was satisfied to powder with corn starch after her Saturday night tub, but you are not. A cosmetic that doesn't have an attractive odor is no longer a cosmetic. Deodorant advertisements all show some shapely girl who is supposed to be attractive, not only because she appears physically adequate, but because she is aromatic as well. There are cosmetics that are used for various parts of the body, all of which must have a fragrance. These include eye-liners, false eyelashes, eyebrow pencils, luscious and sexy creams for the lips, and powder for the face and parts attached thereto. In fact, the whole of a woman's body must have nasal appeal. Any form of cosmetics must give promise of imparting an alluring aroma to the wearer.

With so many products coming in spray cans, a person must exercise extreme care. A friend confessed that she had made an amusing mistake. After her bath, thinking that she was spraying on her usual deodorant, she became aware of an unexpected odor. Checking the label, she was amazed to discover she was holding a can of furniture wax. Though she feared she was only half safe, she was certain she had the shiniest armpits in town.

Body odor is the result of many bodily functions, some normal, some not normal. Perspiration and sebum both come from the skin. They may contain or develop a fatty acid called butyric acid. This same acid is found in certain cheese, in feces, and in vomitus. Once in a lecture on organic chemistry, I was explaining to the class that butyric acid has an individualistic, easily identifiable odor and stated that once you had smelled it, you would never forget it. To illustrate, I passed a small bottle of it around for each student to sniff. Believe me, no one lingered over the opened bottle for long. In fact, the entire procedure was completed in less than two minutes, but the oral complaints and expressions of revulsion lingered on. In a few minutes, several other professors in nearby rooms called in wanting to know what was going on. The secretary of the division chairman called out in the hallway, "For heaven's sake, who died in here?"

The mouth gives forth many stenches. Either these must be covered up or the germs must be killed so that you won't have halitosis and people won't shun you. Halitosis is bad! Almost illegal. You'll be socially degraded, and folks will avoid you unless you gargle with the right mouth wash. Bad breath is known clinically as ozostomia. It's a wonder some producer of TV commercials hasn't latched on to that word. It sounds dangerous and terrific.

My father, the late William Harvey Erb, wrote many poems. While working on this idea of ozostomia, or foul breath, I happened to run across one of his poems, written in 1897. It was entitled, "Matilda." Here it is.

> *The shades of night were falling*
> *Around us thick and fast;*
> *I stood beside Matilda*
> *The first time and the last.*
>
> *She turned her eyes toward heaven—*
> *It was a lovely sight—*
> *The moon kept at me winking,*
> *I pressed her to my side.*
>
> *Her eyes were so bewitching,*
> *It knocked me out of gear;*
> *Her lips were so inviting,*
> *It drove away all fear.*
>
> *I tried to give her kisses*
> *According to etiquette.*
> *But she had eaten onions—*
> *Methinks I smell them yet.*

Various foods and medication cause a change in the odor of some of the body's excreta. After you have been working with turpentine, or taking it internally for medical purposes, your urine may smell of violets. If you took menthol, your urine would be peppermint in odor.

Foods also produce a change in the odor of the feces and

fecal gases. Normally, feces contains such objectional odorants as hydrogen sulfide (a flammable gas), mercaptans, indole, and skatole. Asparagus, cabbage, beans, onions, berries, and eggs increase the putridity of the crepitas, which is a scientific word for flatulence or expelled intestinal gas.

Wouldn't it be a forward step if physiologists could perfect a pill which, when taken with the food, would produce a pleasingly aromatic crepitas? This would be another LSD —Less Smelly Defecations.

Depilatories are preparations designed to remove hair from the body. Hair is a topic of great concern in modern society. Heads are shampooed, scalps are massaged, hair tonics are doused about freely, restorers are employed faithfully. Sometimes people wish to grow hair; other times they desire to remove it. Certain parts of the body, like the armpits and legs, should be hairless if you're a woman, you are told by self-appointed authorities. Cosmetics manufacturers got an idea from the tanneries.

When they tan leather, they must first de-hair the pelt or hide. They place the hairy hide in a vat containing calcium sulfide, or sodium sulfide, or something similar, to dissolve the hair. Such sulfides smell lousy, or terrible, or objectionable, if you don't like the word "lousy," although it is a perfect description. In spite of their stench, they are very efficient for removing hair quickly.

I could put some on my arm and in a few minutes wipe it off, goo, hair, and all. It would look as smooth as a baby's cheek but would smell so bad I couldn't mingle freely with any social group. We chemists concocted depilatories with effective bouquet coverage which mask the unpleasantness of the sulfide stink, and even some with no appreciable smell.

The story of some depilatories dates back to 1924. Out on the Pacific Coast the bubonic plague was raging. When the passengers from foreign lands got off the boats at western ports, the rats jumped ship too and ran inland to have a good time on shore leave. Naturally, they met some of the California rats in the waterfront neighborhoods. The visitors carried bubonic-plague-producing fleas on their backs, which they gladly shared with their newly found friends. Eventually, the squirrels got infected too, and they roamed over a wider district. Scientists said, "We'll have to do something to kill these squirrels to get rid of their fleas."

About this time, over in Germany, a chemist was developing a rodent poison containing a compound called thallium acetate. This proved to be very effective. When the unsuspecting rats nibbled on this stuff, they promptly kicked up four of their legs (their quota) and died with enthusiasm.

Since squirrels are rodents too, they respond in the same way. By this time the squirrels were headed eastward. The worried health authorities knew that if the infected squirrels were not stopped by the time they reached the Sierras, the plague would spread over the entire United States. So they mixed a modification of thallium acetate in paste form with wheat and distributed it all over the woodlands. The squirrels ate and died, and without a host, the fleas starved, checking the extension of the plague.

One notable observation was made. Scientists found that all the dead squirrels were bald. There was a terrific shortage in stoles for milady that year.

One cosmetics manufacturer said, "Maybe there is something in this rat poison that removes hair." Shortly thereafter, he put a product on the market essentially the same as the rat poison containing thallium acetate. Without bothering to test it clinically, he advertised it as an effective and safe way of removing body hair. The result was that some people became blind, while others died. The company no longer exists, at least not by its original name.

Not only is it important to be acceptable personally, but our homes must smell inviting as well. Since ancient times we have pressed odoriferous particles into little blocks or cone-shaped masses which can be burned to floralate a room. Incense, as it is called, comes in a large variety of fragrances and potencies for effective coverage. It is also quite popular to add a perfume to the wax of candles so they can create a seasonal atmosphere as they flicker. These incense candles can be made at home. In December it is nice to put pine oil in the candles so that when the vapor pervades the room it will make it smell like Christmastime.

Bayberry candles are supposed to bring good luck. They are made from the waxy berries of the bayberry plant that grows along the Atlantic shores. You can make your own candles if you live close enough to harvest the berries when they are ripe and waxy. The first step is to heat them in a little pot with water. After the wax has melted, it separates and floats to the surface of the water. Remove the wax, dry it on some paper toweling, and then re-melt it in a fairly deep container, such as an empty tomato-juice can. Dunk a wick or a string into this molten bayberry wax. Draw it out, let it cool, dunk it in again, and let it cool as before. Dunk and cool it many times until the layers build up to the size candle you want. The burning of the bayberry candle at Christmas is a delightfully smelly ritual. It must have the characteristic aroma and be an olive-green color, or no shop will stock it. Who would buy it?

Incense has provided a highly diffusive cover-all for effluvia since Adam threw away the first apple core. Hiding the stench of death and decay was a prime problem with primitive men. They discovered that pleasantly spicy substances pressed into a resin or a gum and set afire would produce a pungent smoke capable of hiding most offensiveness.

In the early temples of worship, where first human sacrifices and then animal sacrifices were placed on the burning altar, something had to disguise the odor of the burnt blood. It smelled to high heaven and evidently heaven did not like it. People began to pass out all over the holy precinct. The worshipers collected the dried, gummy exudations from the aromatic myrrh and frankincense trees, which to them were the acme of fragrance. They threw the gums into the fire with gusto (that was the name of the victim), to see what would happen. They were so pleased with the results that a new industry was born. Incense became so involved with religious rituals that the people began to think of it as holy, rather than just a re-odorant.

By experimentation they learned that the resins from evergreen trees and strong spices would do the same thing. Today we are fond of pine, sandalwood, narcissus, bergamot, and other floral essences. My mother used to scoop a hot coal from the fireplace into a small shovel. On this she sprinkled sugar and walked around the house to spread the odor as it burned. Now we can buy perfumed powders to throw on an open fire to do this.

Even after sacrificial ceremonies went out of fashion, incense continued to be burned in houses of worship, because important dignitaries were buried in the church basement. No matter how well the crypts were sealed, vapors leaked up through porous floors. Every time the vault door was opened to admit a new tenant—wow! Incense burners, with their oriental resinousness, swung from hooks placed at ten-foot intervals. You can be sure of that!

This is no longer a problem with us, but we have problems

of our own. In spite of the fact that we have better methods of garbage disposal and more convenient sanitary facilities than our ancestors did, we still have babies and dogs and cats who don't know where to go—or when.

If you look out the front window just in time to see unexpected visitors arriving, right when something unpleasant has happened—quick, light an incense taper. Always keep some in a handy place near the front door for emergencies. Don't be surprised if your guests get suspicious though. They've probably done the same thing and will recognize the procedure.

Air fresheners in aerosol-can sprayers are easy to use and can change a stink to loveliness. But these may dangerously mask odors that should be a warning, so be sure what you are covering. Suppose coal gas or illuminating gas were leaking into your room without your being aware of it, and instead of turning off the gas or fixing the leak, you sprayed the room with lilac or apple blossoms. That would be the same as telling a warning to shut up, like taking aspirin for a headache.

Another type of air freshener uses a bottle with a wick, which can be pulled out, allowing the chemical to evaporate slowly by capillarity. Some of these wick compounds only seem to destroy odors but actually produce temporary paralysis of the olfactory nerve endings. This can be self-defeating. A fastidious hostess may open one of these bottles before the arrival of her guests and numb her own sense of smell while waiting. When her company comes, they smell the very thing she is trying to hide, until the chemical starts to take effect on them.

There is another way out. An undertaker sought a solution to the problem that some mourners were being made ill by the heavy floral odors in his viewing rooms. By setting up an ozone generator, he was able to kill the odor by ozone-oxidation without spoiling the floral displays. However, too high a concentration of ozone, a poisonous gas, is dangerous; so it is not recommended that the generator be used for too long a time.

Odoriferous materials are absorbed by fats. We have evidence of this in the kitchen. If you expose uncovered butter in the refrigerator right next to an open dish of chopped onions, you are a rotten housekeeper. Those onions will generously disperse their penetrating vapors, which will then be absorbed by the fatty butter. In case this ever does happen, be careful where you apply this altered "well-known spread," unless you are preparing rolls for hamburgers.

Did you ever notice how a cut of cantaloupe or a melon in the refrigerator will force its odor into the butter, or the cream, or other fatty foods? Salami, cheese, fish, and any strongly aromatic food will do the same thing. Make certain such foods are well sealed in jars or plastic bags.

Inside your stomach are fatty substances. If you were to look inside your stomach, you would see it's a mess. Gastric juice coming down in little drops, splashing all around (as they show you on television), and being chased by globules of fat and grease—the whole melee looks like old-fashioned dishwater. As far as its fat content, it is practically the same as dishwater. While you're taking something to counteract acidity, you might drink some detergent to absorb forty-seven times its weight in fat.

What happens when you eat a piece of smelly food like cantaloupe? You cut off a piece of the melon, give it a few quick bites, and it lands in the stomach with a splash. A few minutes later, you burp. Guess what your burp smells like. The odor has been held prisoner in the fat down below until it is expelled with gas. You say, "Darling, that was delicious. It tasted just as good coming up as it did going down." Take the fat out of your stomach and you might belch so sweetly that society would not find the odor offensive. Since you can't do anything about this stomach condition, you have to put breath purifiers in your mouth to hide the nasty odor of your oral explosions.

One thing about our great society is that it is composed of people who have hair. Unfortunately this abundance of hair may cause offense if it is not kept free of oiliness. Your hair contains fat. That's why wallpaper behind a sofa has a greasy spot on it after people have been resting their heads against it for some time. This spot will also absorb odors. If you stay in a room where onions are cooking, the alliaceousness will eventually be picked up by your crowning glory. When I come home after a day in the lab with students experimenting on some current problem, my wife fancies herself a great detective. She has a great ego, but what she likes most about herself is me. She'll say, "You've been making chlorine again," or some such brilliant remark. I can't fool her or tell a lie; the evidence betrays me. The oils of my hair or the wool of my suit (which is also hair) absorbs chlorine or any other odor.

Doctors and bacteriologists, who work closely with strong-smelling antiseptics, carry those smells away with them. The head of our biology department also maintains a private clinical laboratory. You can recognize him by his phenolic odor. Even a sightless person could identify "Old Doc." The nose knows!

We are forced to have woolen clothes cleaned to "destink" them. We must also shampoo our hair frequently to remove the fetid culprit there. As you wash out the soil from your tresses, the odor of soap is being absorbed right back into the hair. That is one of the reasons for adding floral pungency to shampoos.

Wigs made of human hair are not as practical as those made from synthetic fibers. The latter offer a greater resistance to discoloration by the sun, and they will not absorb odors since they have no fat content.

Years ago tar soap was used as a shampoo. You were supposed to smell like an old pitch barrel for that clean feeling. Today, we'd rather have our hair smell of perfume than tar. On leaving a beauty salon, Madame wishes her hair to exude an air of floral delicacy, a symphony of olfaction. But remember this, any soap is effective in cleansing the hair, if you are satisfied with it au naturel.

Woolen cloth has a "new" smell when you first get it. Some say a new smell is as fresh as all outdoors. That might be misleading, especially if you are living near a glue factory, a tire factory, a wood pulp mill, or even a sewage disposal plant. This kind of outdoorsiness doesn't have the bucolic sweetness of a meadow with new-mown hay, clover, and cow manure. The latter is a subtle nitrogen-containing fixative.

Chemists are trying to develop some substance that can be suffused into clothing to prolong the fresh odor of the fabric. One might even spray it on old clothing for rummage sales and flea markets. That would be good smellmanship as well as good salesmanship.

A national magazine devoted to the woolen yarn and knitwear industry asked me to determine whether the odor of wool might influence buyer selection. Many yarn shops are operated in connection with private homes. Household odors, from the kitchen, etc., come in contact with open yarn packages, which may absorb the smells and become objectionable to the buyer. We studied many types of woolen yarns that had been exposed to various atmospheres of floral, spicy, and putrid odors. Invariably the wools that had absorbed the pleasant aromas, even if only in insignificant amounts, were the favorite selection of all women tested, though the same brand of wool was involved in all test series.

Retailers have found by experimenting that such items as hosiery sell much more quickly if delicately perfumed. Stockings may be made of nylon, rayon, or even cotton. Whatever fiber is used, whether natural or synthetic, the chemical processes used give it a "fabric" odor. Most people do not recognize it, but it is there just the same.

Dr. Donald A. Laird of Colgate University was interested in determining just how much scent affected the customer's selection of hose. Several groups of hose of identical quality were placed on display. One group had no additive, just the odor of raw nylon. Each of the other groups had a different floral aroma. No mention of this was made on the displays. The female customers looked, touched, pulled, and stretched, but selected in the following manner:

PERCENTAGE OF CUSTOMERS PREFERRING VARIOUS NYLONS

Smell	First 72 Women	Next 83 Women	All 250 Women
Narcissus odor	49.8	50.8	50.0
Fruity odor	24.9	22.8	24.0
Sachet perfume	16.8	18.0	18.0
Natural	8.5	8.4	8.0

What does it all prove? For one thing, it strongly suggests that women are subsconsciously influenced by odor. Some of the women insisted the odoriferous stockings were the more durable. Another conclusion is that among the scents tested narcissus is the favorite. Men fall for products with eye appeal—especially leggy advertisements, while women have an olfactory response. It is similar to the subliminal technique in advertising.

Climate, especially temperature, plays a role in odor acceptance. People in warm countries apparently take to products with a higher fragrance concentration.

To keep your secretary or stenographer happy and sweet-looking all day, office equipment and office supplies are taking on a luringly pleasant aroma. Carbon paper and typewriter ribbon come in different scents, and a special pencil can be had which is spicy smelling for a spicy girl. She may sniff it while she is writing. These odoriferous pencils have a great turn-over, but most of them turn up at home.

Fashion dictates that we have leather belts, leather shoes, and leather wallets and pocketbooks. Nothing really takes the place of leather. It has a delightful nitrogeny smell that has always made an olfactory imprint on men and women. Fortunately we can reproduce the smell of a tanned animal hide chemically.

Manufacturers of plastic materials for shoes had many problems to overcome. Although they created a reasonable imitation of the appearance of leather, something was lacking. Customers seemed to have no confidence in the new product until the plastic was impregnated with the man-made odor of leather. Smell sells!

A camel-skin harness worn by an elephant might cause a mighty stampede.

Leather is one of the old, old products. Cave men wore animal skins. Ten thousand years ago American Indians knew how to tan it. Tombs of Egyptian kings contained leather articles placed there more than five thousand years ago.

De-haired pelts or hides formerly were thrown into a solution of chicken manure, cow dung, or dog dung and water and allowed to partially disintegrate—a smelly process. For centuries this was by far the most unpleasant process in tanneries. Later, the investigation of the active organic constituents of the dung infusion led to the use of enzymes such as trypsin, a protein-digestive enzyme that is present in dung. The process became known as *bating*.

After a few days in this bath, the hides are thrown into a vegetable solution made of leaves, roots, and bark from various trees. The tannins in this vegetable mash do the trick. Tannin or tannic acid is found in tea leaves, coffee beans, nut galls, and the bark of certain trees. You can prove that there is tannic acid in your tea, coffee, and cola beverages. When iron comes into contact with a solution of tannic acid, a blue-black iron tannate is formed. This is ink. Therefore, all you have to do is add a solution of an iron salt to a cup of tea or coffee, and when it turns dark blue-black, you can know you're drinking ink. The old black coffee of grandma's time, which was brewed in an *iron* pot on the back of the kitchen range all day long, owed its blackness to iron ink, not to strength. Grandma could have written a letter with it if she had only known how to write.

If you were led blindfolded into a shoe store, you would instinctively recognize the characteristic odor. You know a doctor's office too, the same way. The smell tells. I advise premedical students that when they begin their practice of medicine, they should put certain odoriferous chemicals in their waiting rooms to make them smell more professional. Thymol, a crystalline alcohol, is one type that can be put

behind frames of diplomas, licenses, and such in the phy-
sician's outer room to give an antiseptic, clinical impression.
Iodoform might be used too.

There is a peculiar museum-like mustiness in a library,
made more noticeable by the subdued hush-hush. When I
am engrossed in a lively TV program, it is not unknown for
me to fail to notice that sparks from my pipe are burning a
hole in my shirt. But when the audio-visual stimuli are
played down, our osmic responses become more acute. Well,
the tomb-like edifice for books smells of mildewed bind-
ings, library paste, aging paper, worn covers, and thumbed
pages. Paper absorbs many odors during the handling that
books and periodicals get in a busy public library. Ventilation is usually not of the best, especially in the stack rooms.
This may contribute to the ancient-paper smell that eventually fills the whole building.

Old saliva also adds to the atmosphere. We have two
types of literary browsers, the thumb lickers and the finger
lickers. The thumb licker moistens his pressure digit with
his tongue, then shoves upward against each page to insure
turning only one at a time. Paging from the bottom up,
he leaves his saliva on the lower margins. The finger licker
slides his moistened pointing digit downward, leaving the
offensive saliva on the top margins. After years of such un-
sterile usage, many different layers of saliva pile up on the
pages. Even fresh spittle has an unpleasant odor (unless it's
in your own mouth), so what can you expect of the public's
dried saliva, ripened with age? WARNING: Your library
may be infectious.

Speaking of infectiousness, before modern clinical test-
ing was available, physicians often relied on their sense of
smell for diagnosing diseases. The doctor in those days had
to see, hear, feel, and smell his patient. It is well known

that diabetic individuals have a peculiarly sweet breath, due to the presence of acetone. Sometimes urine was tasted to ascertain the suspected presence of sugar. Smallpox, then a common ailment, had a most objectionable, distinctive odor. Favus, a contagious skin disease, was described as having a moldy, mousy smell, while another, pemphigus, characterized by blisters, had its own fetid odor. A so-called "butcher shop" odor was given off by yellow-fever patients. The smell of diphtheria was described as sickeningly sweetish. In chronic nephritis (Bright's disease) the breath may be ammoniacal and offensive. Today little emphasis is put on osmic diagnosis in medical schools, because many of these diseases have been eradicated, and also because of more positive diagnostic techniques.

In certain mental conditions, known as osmophobia, there is an abnormal dread of odors.

De-hospitalizing the atmosphere of the sick room by substituting floral aromas for the usual medicinal smells might hasten recoveries. There may be a scent-therapy in our future! Smell and get well!

One eats periodically, one drinks occasionally, but breathing—that one does continuously. The things most necessary for life are wholesome, flavorful food for the thoughtful diner, pure water and harmless beverages for the drinker, and above everything, good, clean air at all times for those who expect to breathe.

Observe a ribbon of smoke rise, cobra-like, into the air. It sways and is fanned lightly by delicate atmospheric currents, but it finally disappears. Or does it? To the eye, yes; but actually the smoke is still in the air. The particles have been dispersed by the process known as diffusion. While no longer discernible as a stream of smoke, the particles are invisibly diffused through a much greater volume of air. They will unconsciously be inhaled. What you can't see can still hurt you.

Air sewage is on the increase. The pollutants are not only dusts, pollens, smokes, and other solids, but many gases. If the gases do not have a smell, we do nothing about them; when they are offensive, aroused communities make organized protests very loud and clear. However, it is not the olfactory foulness of the air—which is only a nuisance—for which we must have primary concern but the unseen irritants and poisons riding piggyback. The future security of our national health is at stake.

Many of the odorous air contaminants are of industrial origin. Fertilizer manufacturers, tanneries, chemical industries, textile factories, paper mills, petroleum refineries, breweries, pharmaceutical plants, canners, and food processors are some of the guilty industrial polluters. Municipal dumps, settling ponds, and other disposal facilities also contribute to atmospheric stenches.

Effective methods for controlling and eliminating such industrial odors must be instituted. Reluctance to enforce existing antipollution laws is no doubt largely political. Many of the big industrial firms, besides contributing daily to air pollution, also contribute heavily to political parties.

Some insectologists maintain that the butterfly is becoming extinct. The explanation is not known, but the suggestion has been offered that with the increasing concentration of air pollutants, the female butterfly can't smell the male, or vice versa, and without a mama butterfly, no babies.

We should not dismiss lightly such *nonodorous* gaseous air pollutants as carbon monoxide, being spewed out continuously by all motor vehicles. Next to having convenient transportation to and from the place where we earn our bread and butter, our second reason for wanting a car is usually so that we can drive out for some fresh air in the great open spaces. Oh, to inhale the bucolic sweetness of a meadow, or the ozone cleanliness of the atmosphere after a thunderstorm! To get there we leave a trail of exhaust fumes that cancel much of the ambrosial fragrance nature has offered. We and fifty million others are doing the contaminating together. In union there is stench!

There are many ways of banishing unwanted odors. One way is to burn them. One day while I was lecturing to a class, I noticed that one fellow was striking matches one after another. Since this is an unorthodox way of being unattentive in class, I asked him what he was doing. "There is something stinking back here and I'm trying to burn it up," he explained hectically. He was attempting to oxidize, or burn, the bad smell. It would take a bonfire to clear the air in most chemistry classes.

Society, with all its complexities and ramifications, is truly a sensual conglomeration of living individuals. It relies on seeing, hearing, and feeling for its contacts and its communications. Its moods, its emotions are constantly influenced by the sense of smell.

Although the sense of smell is a subtle force in social problems, nevertheless in many ways it is just as powerful as the more apparent stimuli of the other senses. A society released from the influences of odor would undoubtedly be entirely different. Even the elephants might not want to stay in the same enclosures with us.

Deodorization must be handled with care!

5!
The Smell of Vacations
and Home

SUMMER IS THE SEASON for vacations. It is also the season
when highway departments tear up the regular highways
and open the detours. Everybody likes to make a change.
But why? Psychologically you need an occasional change
of surroundings and smell. If you're living in a stinky environment, you want to get away from it and into an atmosphere that is different, to say the least, just as the elephant
ran away from the camel.

When you get two weeks off after working fifty, the first thing you want to do, if you live near the coast, is to go to the seashore to smell the salt air. You think audibly, "Ah, this is the place to be. Salt air!" Other people want to go to the mountains to inhale the cool resinousness of pine trees, or if they are skiers, to smell the synthetic snow.

Scenic mountain beauty and its pure invigorating air is a strong attraction. Well, the beauty is undeniable, but whether the air is actually pure is another question. Professor Fritz Went, a biometeorologist from the University of Nevada has revealed that trees foul the air with ten times more pollutants than all of man's fires, factories, and fast cars.

Pine trees and sage bushes produce the "blue haze" seen frequently in the summer even in very remote areas not likely to be contaminated by man-made products. They emit highly toxic terpenes and esters which react in sunshine to form a smog not unlike that found in industrial areas. The haze from sage actually inhibits other vegetation. Fortunately, the smog is usually purged from the atmosphere by precipitation before it reaches dangerous concentrations.

Still other people prefer the brackish, dead-fishiness of a lake-front resort where the family is crowded into a couple of rooms reeking of insect repellents and the algal mustiness of wet bathing suits. When they open the window for ventilation, all they get is a suffocating acroleinity from the exhaust fan of the restaurant next door.

That's what we call a vacation and we're willing to pay for it. I often marvel at people who leave a perfectly good home, with a perfectly good olfactory environment, to go to another spot where the conveniences are inadequate; but subconsciously the change of aroma helps to give them a different feeling. They think it's a lark although the place smells like a dead sea gull. They think it gives them status. It's rewarding to have people ask, "Where were you? Such a nice coat of tan! In Florida, in California, New Mexico, or where?" We do love to brag and show photographs and exaggerate about how our olfactory horizons have been broadened by travel. We may even lie a little to avoid describing any unpleasantness. We think it is worth the sacrifice to save millions of dollars in vacation clubs all year (at no interest), merely to get away from one smell into another.

Oh yes, those Diesel smells, which you inhale when you get behind a truck or bus, are the odors of "happy motoring." A vacation on wheels between motels.

How nice it smells to be back home again! If you're not traveling, you're probably at home. Home is where you can scratch any place that itches. The domicile in which you are supposed to live, move, and pay taxes, is a strange place sometimes.

If you have just purchased a new rancher or split-level, you have a promise of a fresh olfactory experience. New plaster, new wood, new paint, and wallpaper with the aroma of the paste beneath it are still evident. You initially come into nasal contact with this new, new smell the moment the real-estate operator opens the door to the "sample home." The physical appearance and the quality of construction of the house is not the entire attraction.

However, most of you don't dwell in a new house, but rather in an old house that has been occupied by other tenants. You inherited or acquired it by devious means. You love this old house of yours with its characteristic, personalized odor. It's yours—all yours. It smells like you. It smells like your wife, if you have a wife, or your husband, or the sweet nitrogeny odor of the baby (who can also smell peculiar sometimes). It may savor of your uncle or your aunt, your dog or your cat.

In the distinctiveness of your home there is an amalgamation of many olfactory experiences and accidents. The foody steam from the overworked kitchen, the clean, soapiness of the laundry, fragrant flowers from the house plants, and cosmetics from the bedroom are just a few of the smells your dwelling possesses. If you're a smoker, the home smells of stale tobacco or cigar butts.

Yes, tobacco and its smoke can completely permeate the home. For variety some blends have aromatic substances added to give them distinctiveness. Fruit and flower smells are incorporated with the tobacco, but all cigarettes, except the rum-and-maple variety and the mentholated, have such uniformity of smell that most people cannot tell one brand from the other. Here, too, the trade names and the advertising pitch have much to do with the buyer's selection.

Our cigarette packages carry a warning that cigarette smoking may be dangerous to the smoker's health. Although this sensible warning goes unheeded in most cases, it is known that certain tars in the smoke from cigarettes are carcinogens. They have the power to produce cancer, especially of the lungs. The fact that it is almost impossible not to inhale cigarette smoke makes this form of smoking the most dangerous. Cigarette smokers, because they inhale, absorb more smoke than non-cigarette smokers. The inner lung surface has an area about five hundred times greater than the entire outer body surface. Again, the ease with which cigarettes can be smoked makes it possible for both young and old to inhale more or less continuously throughout the day.

Because manufacturers have included filter tips and have done much to reduce some carcinogenic substances from

cigarette smoke, they are like a widow's stepchild—cut off
without a scent. Aromatics, such as coumarin and ionone
(which comes from violets), are added to mask the overpowering acridity of the burning weed.

It's a peculiar thing—when a girl is being courted by a
male victim who is a pipe-smoker, she says, "Oh, that smells
good! I just love your pipe." She has used the word "love"
for the first time. Then he blows out a cloud of smoke in
his happiness. But beware; she's only trying to trap him.
He thinks he is courting her, but all the time she's planning
on his capitulation. She tells him that his pipe smells sweet
and that he smells sweet, even though he knows he has
bromhidrosis. After they are married, the "sweet-smelling"
pipe that used to dangle between his teeth becomes a *smelly*
pipe. She now screams, "You, and your stinky old pipe."
The living room becomes offensive and the bedroom ex-
poses his habit of smoking before going to bed.

A little poem I first read in a college comic magazine
comes to mind. I do not know who wrote it:

> *Tobacco is a dirty weed,*
>   *I like it.*
> *It satisfies no earthly need,*
>   *I like it.*
> *It makes you sick,*
> *It makes you lean,*
> *It takes the hair right off your bean,*
> *The worst darn stuff, I've ever seen,*
>   *I like it.*

Let us consider some of the specific rooms in the house.
The kitchen, a source of numerous elusive and highly individualistic odors, is the locale of most of the activities
and most of the accidents in the home. Sometimes food

prepared in this room tastes like an accident, but more often it creates an aromatic magic. How can you resist the sweet fruitiness of baking pies, the heavy richness of beef roasting, or the tantalizing sizzle of frying bacon? On the other hand, you cannot overlook the unpleasant odors, because they speak for themselves.

When food is being fried, the heat of the pan breaks up the fat into two parts, glycerol (glycerine) and fatty acids. This, of course, takes place when the pan is hotter than necessary. Now if at this point the woman who is doing the cooking answers the phone or doorbell, permitting the glycerol to overheat still more, she generates a teargas called acrolein—an unsaturated aldehyde that is very, very irritating and, if concentrated, is very poisonous. It makes your eyes water and your nose dribble, and makes you feel most uncomfortable. If you got too much it could kill you. It's a war gas. Acrolein or acrylic aldehyde will not confine itself to the kitchen but permeates the dining area, the living room, and the entire house. A good cook should never allow the frying pan to get hot enough to decompose or degrade the glycerol into acrolein.

It is difficult to mask the piercing, sulfurousness of any member of the cabbage family, which includes broccoli, Brussels sprouts, sauerkraut, etc. These foods must be subject to claustrophobia because they kick up such a fuss when boiled in a covered kettle.

When we come to the bathroom, and sooner or later we have to, we not only detect assorted florescent toilet preparations but also highly personal odors from body effluvia. Because we no longer go to the little house out back, it is inevitable that in modern homes the odor from the bathroom oozes throughout the other parts of the house. Architects have not designed the location of the average bathroom properly. It should be right in the center of the residential structure with an exhaust fan forcing ventilation upward through a skylight or proper vent. All the household odors would be drawn out through the bathroom instead of the reverse.

Bless the man who first discovered how to create enough pressure to have running water even on upper levels. The first time my grandfather visited my parents' city home, he was appalled to learn that our "outhouse" was indoors. He thought it was a revolting, filthy idea.

The Pennsylvania Dutch still refer to "going out," even when they have modern sanitary facilities. One day when I was shopping in Hess Brothers' magnificent department store in Allentown, I overheard a woman say to a saleslady, "I came in to go out. Where is it?"

The familiar odors of this essential room come from the feces and urine of the human body. Your foods, hygiene and occupational pursuits determine how your lavatory is going to smell. Of course, you don't spend all of your time in the bathroom. I usually have a set of paperbacks on a strategically placed shelf where I can read lots of material while I'm using the little room. It's a good place to catch up on my reading since it is the only room in the house where I am permitted to be alone. A very important spot, especially at various crises in your daily life.

Let's go down to the cellar. If you don't have a basement, you need not pay attention. The nether part of the house develops a peculiar air of musty plaster, moist wall paint, moldy, discarded furniture, and mildewed floors, and it generally feels dampish. That is because it *is* damp, as a rule. By removing the water content of the air, you can get rid of these odors. Electric dehumidifiers can take the water out of the damp atmosphere and condense it, but they should be hooked up to a drainage system so that the condensed water actually leaves the premises and is not permitted to re-evaporate into the room. Calcium chloride will also pull the water out of the air to make it drier, but it becomes a messy, gooey mass. Using silica gel is better because it does not become so drippy wet and can be re-used by drying it out in a warm oven.

The furnishings and products used in the home contribute their share to its characteristic odor. Throughout the house wood is the favorite material used in the construction of furniture. Through chemistry we are now making our wood more fragrant. Some woods, such as cedar, sandalwood, fruitwood, rosewood, and some types of mahogany, are naturally aromatic. Most people can't afford the genuine article, because it seems that, when something has an odoriferous imprint, its price goes up. Imitation aromatics are added to lumber of inferior grade, along with the veneer, to resemble any wood desired. Inexpensive pieces of pine or cypress can be treated with synthetic compounds that will deceive all but those skilled in identifying the difference in grain. For example, you don't have to buy cedar anymore. You can obtain oil of cedarwood and impregnate any wood used for constructing a clothes closet or a "cedar chest."

The newest idea is to give bedroom furniture the aroma of lilacs, violets, or roses. Of course, when you are asleep, it probably doesn't matter. Who wants to stay up all night just to smell the furniture? Chairs for men can be given a tobacco-mellowness. The pungency of aromatic tobacco would be there before you light up your "old stinky pipe." There is an olfactory future in the furniture business.

Many householders who attempt do-it-yourself projects can't abide the odor of paint. I like it, but some individuals

claim that it makes them ill, producing symptoms of a
cold, an upset stomach, or ingrown toenails. Maybe it's
true, I don't know. To overcome this objection, today's
manufacturers attempt to produce an odorless paint. How
odorless can a paint be? Almost completely. Chemicals are
added to either cancel or mask the offensive factor. One
terrific innovation was the introduction of various floral
oils that effectively cover the paint odor. These are especially useful when redecorating rooms in hospitals or sick
rooms at home where there are invalids who cannot be
moved. Since hospitals are the fifth largest business in the
country, comfort of the patients is an important considera-
tion. Pleasant rather than painty or clinical smells are a
comfort.

Untreated raw paper has a rather peculiar odor that is
unpleasant to some people. This odor can be counteracted
by various types of chemical compounds. Flowered wallpaper in the future may carry a floral scent to match the
print.

Newspaper advertising already makes use of various
types of odoriferous ink. A merchant may wish to empha-
size a sale of watermelons at a bargain price. If the colored
picture is printed with ink containing a simulated odor
of watermelon, every subscriber to the local newspaper will
be aware of the bargain and may find it irresistible. Another
advertiser may want to whet your appetite for butter or
lemonade by using a yellow ink of appropriate odor. The
smell will sell but may get out of hand. Imagine a daily
paper with ads of different odors on every page. The total
conglomeration might be highly objectionable. You would
not be attracted by an ad for a man's suit that smells like
the beefsteak pictured on the opposite page. Complications

of odor sensations might be worse than complications of diseases.

Carpeting has an unusual odor when it is first produced. This is caused by the weaving material, the sizing, the rubber backing, the woolen yarns, and, above all, the dyes. The latter can smell like a wet, mangy dog, believe me. Rugs now come with odorant compounds added. Before the manufacturers realized the value of making carpeting more aromatic, they applied suggestive names—such as mulberry, burnt orange, cinnamon, and rose—hoping that the name alone would stimulate an olfactory recall. It did not help much.

The family car, which is like a second home to many of us because we spend so much time in it, also reflects the personal osmic atmosphere of the owner. An old one may possess the heavy pungency of stained, beaten-up upholstery, old sweat shirts left on the back seat, wet bathing suits, almost anything spilled on the old floor mats, babies' diapers slightly used, or even garbage in the trunk. The possibilities are limited only by our imagination.

How you love a new car! Not only does it have visual appeal because of its shininess and color, but that "new-car smell" is absolutely captivating. It gets you right in your pocketbook. The delicate air of the fresh upholstering, the newness of the rubber, the discreetness of the paint, the modern plastics, and the overall metallic scent all blend harmoniously to break down your sales resistance.

Knowing this, used-car dealers have applied chemical techniques for effective camouflage of their older models. Not only is the exterior repainted and the chrome shined but the interior of the car, the trunk, and under the hood is sprayed with compounds to give the prospective buyer a new-car smell. All the rubber is treated with a synthetic "new rubberiness," and the upholstering is tinted with a perfumed dye. Even the old motor can be chemically cleaned and given a metallic freshness so that it appears unused or, at least, hardly used.

To aid himself in making a decision, a customer may kick the tires and ask about the mileage and the former owner, but the applied aroma is what makes the sale. There is more to this than meets the eye, or the nostrils. In this case the nose doesn't know, so what you don't know may hurt you.

While cars must smell new, other commodities must have the tonality of age. You wouldn't want the items of an antique shoppe to smell brand new. Here we must reverse the idea. Clever crooks can give newly made "antiques" a scent of great age and mustiness. After the wood is distressed and shot with buckshot to produce worm holes, it is sprayed to provide a highly diffusive coverage for the green resinousness of the new wood. The article will finally look old and smell older.

6!
The Smell of Cleanliness

OUR LIFE is one long battle against a demon called "Dirt." Dirt on our bodies, in our homes, in our community, in the water, in the air we breathe, or on someone's tongue. Filth not only looks repulsive to us but is always accompanied by odors that repel.

The grime can usually be washed away or hidden from sight, but the indiscreet scent lingers spitefully on, and on, and on. If we cannot eradicate it, we try to neutralize it.

If this fails, we mask it with a more pungent, pleasant fragrance that is purposely attention-getting. This is like biting one's lip to overpower the pain of a stubbed toe.

As a rule, not only do we like to have clean bodies, but after a shower we like to advertise our cleanliness. Having learned that skin albumin is soluble in water, I'm afraid to bathe often, so I frequently anoint myself with various clean-smelling materials so people will think I'm a clean person. As a matter of fact, I'm really dirty but I smell clean. You can save a lot on your water bills and on your sewer rentals by repeated bodily applications of clean, aromatic solutions.

Soap for bathing didn't come into general use until the seventeenth century. Although it had been made for thousands of years before that, it was mostly reserved for medicinal purposes. Because it was usually made from the rancid fat of meat scraps or old blubber accumulated over long periods, it was most unsavory. One who bore this particular stench was said to be clean.

Later, when soap was made of oil from the tropical palm and coconut tree, its strange mildness was considered evil and the clergy preached against its use. Well, no one put up too much of a fight because bathing was still just an occasional adventure. After the decline of Rome, public baths had been discontinued as pagan, and bathing was frowned on even in private. With the introduction of milder soap, the practice of bathing was still in its infancy; that is, only infants were being washed.

It wasn't until 1900 that the medical profession realized the danger of wearing dirty, bacteria-laden clothes too long and the importance of frequent baths. They discovered that fumes of ammonia and other vapors emanating from clothing worn for a lengthy period were not harmful in themselves, but were indicative of the presence of bacteria that could be. The malodorous, poorly ventilated hamper in the bathroom sometimes reeks with such vigor that we are tempted to hold services over it.

The first quarter of this century, we still felt clean if we gave forth the medicinal smell of "green soap," and one very popular soap that emphasized its deodorizing quality even added phenol. It is only in very recent times that floral additives have been popular.

These have made such a hit, we now demand perfumed bath oils and lotions, after-shave lotions, pre-shave lotions, foot balms, dusting powder, etc. Women insist on aromatic make-up bases. In addition, they dab cologne behind their ears, on their wrists, and in other strategic geographical locations. No one wants to smell of ordinary soap. Toilet soap may be perfumed with rose, lilac, violet, or narcissus, additives designed to mask the lye–fatty-acidness of the raw soap.

Parents are in a precarious position. Whenever an occasion arises when they should receive a gift, their children often present them with some type of toilet item. It's only by chance if the aromas don't clash. Mother should select a favorite scent like she selects a silver pattern, so her family and friends will buy her something that blends with it. Remember, besides the above, her hair spray, deodorant, and nail polish have odors to be considered.

The word "soap" isn't fashionable anymore. You must use a detergent, they tell us in strong language. Whether you use the word "detergent" or the word "soap," you're still dealing with detergents. The dictionary defines detergent as "any cleaning agent." Now, if you have a woman coming into your house to clean—she's a cleaning agent and, therefore, a detergent. If you wash up the kitchen floor, you're a detergent. Old-fashioned soap is a detergent because it is a cleaning agent. Actually, detergents should be classified as: (1) soap detergents, and (2) non-soap detergents. The word "soap" has been pushed aside, and detergent is getting all the attention by advertising copy writers.

Soap is one of the oldest types of detergent in the world. It is easy to make and is sometimes made in the home. If you go into the Pennsylvania Dutch area, like the good old Lehigh Valley, you'll find that the people there save their fats in cans and old buckets during the long winter months. Comes spring, and the appearance of the first robin and the new blanket of green o'er all the fields reminds them that the time will soon be upon them to store the clothes they wore all winter. Before it gets too warm, the women will have to replenish their supply of laundry soap to fortify against that great laundering day. They take their old fats and oils and the old fatty meat scraps to one particular home, the hostess home. This year, Mrs. Hoffadeckle may be the hostess. Maybe next year, Mrs. Zook, and so on down the line. It's really like going to a party where you'll meet friends you haven't seen all year and learn the latest juicy gossip.

Everyone dumps the accumulated fats into one enormous iron kettle, and then the stuff is boiled with lye and stirred and stirred for hours with each lady taking a turn at the ladle. Meanwhile, they are eating and having games. By the end of the day, the pot has a big, thick blob of soap in it, which they pour out into different molds or boxes. When it hardens, they cut it into small blocks and every person takes home her proportional share based on the weight of fat she contributed to the pot originally. A wonderful time is had by all. Since it's soap-making time, clean fun is the order of the day.

Remember grandma's lye soap? It was a good cleaner, a good detergent. If the soap didn't clean you, the lye did, and between the two, they made a clean sweep of it—mighty clean, often down to the bone.

When a naturally occurring fat or oil is hydrolyzed, as it is in the iron kettle containing lye solution, it breaks down into glycerol and fatty acids. Glycerol (or, as it is commonly called, glycerine) is present in all fats. The fatty acids are different depending upon the kind of fat or oil that is being hydrolyzed. The most common are palmitic, stearic, and oleic acids. The first two are solids, the third is a liquid at ordinary room temperature. A soap is actually a water-soluble sodium salt of one or more of the fatty acids. With a liquid fatty acid, like oleic acid, you can make instant soap by merely adding a solution of strong lye to it.

The following table shows some common fats and oils and their fatty-acid content.

SOME COMMON FATS AND OILS

Fat or Oil	Fatty Acids (in the form of glyceryl esters)
Butterfat (cow's milk)	Butyric, caproic, capric, palmitic, stearic, oleic acids
Cacao butter (cacao nibs)	Palmitic, oleic, stearic, myristic acids
Coconut oil	Caproic, caprylic, capric, lauric acids
Cod-liver oil	Oleic, myristic, palmitic, stearic acids
Cottonseed oil	Oleic, stearic, palmitic, linoleic acids

Fat or Oil	Fatty Acids (in the form of glyceryl esters)
Human fat	Stearic, palmitic, oleic, butyric, caproic acids
Lard (pig fat)	Stearic, palmitic, oleic, linoleic acids
Linseed oil (flax seed)	Linoleic, linolenic, oleic, palmitic, myristic acids
Maize oil (corn oil)	Arachidic, stearic, palmitic, oleic acids
Menhaden oil (menhaden fish)	Palmitic, myristic, oleic, stearic acids
Mustard oil (seeds)	Erucic, arachidic, stearic, oleic acids
Neat's-foot oil (cattle hoofs)	Palmitic, stearic, oleic acids
Olive oil	Linoleic, oleic, arachidic acids
Palm oil (seed)	Palmitic, lauric, oleic acids
Peanut oil	Arachidic, linoleic, hypogaeic, palmitic acids
Poppy-seed oil	Linoleic, isolinolenic, palmitic, stearic acids
Rape-seed oil	Erucic, arachidic, stearic acids
Sperm oil (blubber of sperm whale)	Oleic, palmitic acids
Tallow (ox or sheep fat)	Stearic, palmitic, oleic acids

You will notice that butyric acid, a definitely malodorous acid, is present in butter and more especially in rancid butter. Human fat also contains some, as do sweat, muscles, feces, etc.

A non-soap detergent is made in much the same way as a soap, except that, instead of being the sodium salt of a fatty acid, it is the sodium salt of a sulfonic acid obtained from petroleum. These non-soap detergents have one advantage, they will clean well in hard water. A soap in hard water produces an insoluble scum. That's what makes the ring around the bathtub. Next to the wedding ring, that's the second ring the bride gets after she's married. She struggles with this ring the rest of her life unless she uses a non-soap detergent. The scum is an insoluble calcium soap caused by the high calcium content in the hard water. With a non-soap detergent, there is none of this insoluble salt formed; consequently the clothes look whiter, the bathtub is ringless, and you should look cleaner and shinier. If you have soft or relatively soft water, ordinary soap detergents are just as good and possibly a little cheaper.

The soap that you use is also designed to remove your excess body odor. Everyone has a body odor, which is determined by his health, occupation, individual and national eating habits, and environment. To the Oriental, the American smells of butter; while to us, Orientals smell fishy. Central Europeans can't conceal the scent of the cabbage, turnips, and radishes they consume in such abundance. The first thing we notice about an Eskimo is his blubber odor, and about a native of India, the rice and spices in his diet. In the nursery we learn, "Fee, Fi, Fo, Fum, I smell the blood of an Englishman." The mildest and most attractive human odor is the palm oil and fruitiness of South Sea Islanders.

In an experiment several years ago, a woman acted as a guinea pig. I think her last name was Pig. Mrs. Ginny Pig! An attempt was made, at her request, to remove her body odor entirely. After certain manipulations and chemical applications, they did succeed in making her odor-free temporarily, but she was very, very uncomfortable. She couldn't get along with herself because she couldn't identify herself with her nose. It made her feel like a stranger, and for the first time she began to appreciate her former state. Her husband must have liked her natural smell too or he wouldn't have married her.

Yes, everyone has his own personal odor, but he gets so used to it he no longer notices it. I'm glad I smell like Russell C. Erb and not like James Conroy or somebody like that. If James Conroy is reading this now, I mean it. I smell the way I do and I'm thankful for it. It could be worse.

In the community where my wife used to live before she succumbed to my charms, there was a general handy man who was an industrious, dependable workman. Everyone called him to repair odds and ends because he did such a thorough job. The only hitch was he never bathed or changed his clothing from one year's end to another. In his battle for cleanliness, he stopped at nothing—that is exactly where he stopped. The only time that he donned a new outfit was when the old one wore out completely. When asked why he didn't bathe, he said, "Why bother? I would only get dirty again. No one asks me to do clean jobs." Once he took a bath before appearing in court as a witness, and nobody recognized him. He could have said with Shakespeare, "O! my offense is rank, it smells to heaven."

All the children in town used to delight in teasing him with a parody of "That's Peggy O'Neil." They nicknamed him "B. O. For-real," and the lyrics ran like this:

> *If his clothes are filthy gray,*
> *That's B. O. For-real.*
> *If he sweats at work all day,*
> *That's B. O. For-real.*

If he jumps, and he's filled with wrath,
Every time we shout, "Go take a bath,"
Full of putridity, also rancidity,
That's B. O. For-real.

Detergents can remove or hide a person's body odor but they, in turn, also have an odor all their own. For this reason, many odoriferous things are added to make them more generally acceptable.

In some instances, laundry detergents have chemicals added to give our clothes an ozone freshness. Despite this, no chemical can improve on the joyous, cozy odor of freshly laundered sheets, air-dried out of doors in the sunshine rather than in an automatic drier.

If we can't wash soil away—we bleach it away. It's somewhat like surgery: if you can't cure something, you cut it out. You're not cleaning when you bleach. The dirt is still there but it doesn't look like dirt anymore. An ordinary pan of dirt with bleach added wouldn't look the same either. You are not bleaching soil *from* the clothing. You are merely changing its color. However, bleaching is an important operation. According to TV, housewives are forever talking about their wash and how they can see which is whiter, clear across the laundromat. Personally, I have never met such women. Talk, yes, but not about the whiteness of Uncle Simon's underdrawers.

Bleaches have a very prominent smell. They are usually chlorine compounds, but chlorine is also very effective in the pure state. You could buy a tank of chlorine gas for your laundry and run the gas directly into your washing machine, but this method would be entirely too dangerous and cumbersome and your washer might disintegrate. It is far better to use preparations that will release chlorine efficiently, as needed, and with less danger.

Waxing and polishing are shining examples of big cleaning and touch-up procedures in the home. There is no need for floor waxes to have a waxy, oily, irritating odor since things can be added to give them a more pleasant tonality. This also applies to furniture polishes (one brand smells like the war gas chloroacetophenone). A health-food addict might stimulate her appetite with a treated polish on her tables savoring of magnolia, or she might like to sit on a lemon chair one day, an orange chair the next, and then huckleberry for variety. Maybe she would even enjoy a dinette with the scent of peanut butter and crackers, or chocolate soda. For those with a romantic flare, a polish with a smell of delicate florescence accompanied by perfumed candlelight could do the trick. Shoe polish too, will manifest the heavy odor of nitrobenzene or oil of bitter almonds unless there are incorporated discreet perfumes to effectively cover the raw unpleasantness.

For heavy-duty household cleaning nothing excels ammonia, a colorless, pungent gas put into water to form a solution called *ammonium hydroxide* when concentrated and *ammonia water* when weak. It is pretty strong stuff regardless of the name and could be lethal if inhaled full-strength. It may have received its name from the oasis of Jupiter Ammon in the Sahara Desert, where it arose from decomposing camel dung.

From time immemorial women have found ammonia indispensable as a cleaning agent because it is weakly basic (and so is harmless to the skin), emulsifies grease and fat, and leaves no residue to be wiped away. It simply evaporates. Now, all of a sudden we are led to believe that some startling new discovery has been made. A cleaning product with a label stating "Ammonia Added" is really revolutionary. Is it? Old Pharaoh's slaves used ammonia to swab the marble palace floors.

When concentrated, it is powerfully corrosive and must be diluted in water to be safely used. The label on the bottle you purchase at the store warns you to use one part of ammonia to eight or ten parts of water. The vapor would floor you were it any stronger.

One day I obtained some concentrated ammonium hydroxide for my wife, to be used at spring-housecleaning time. It was in an ordinary glass bottle which I had not yet labeled. Placing it on the kitchen counter, I swiftly departed, expecting my wife to store it in the place of her choice. That's what I always do with everything—just drop whatever I have in the most convenient spot, expecting someone else to put it away. My wife growls but it usually works out to my satisfaction.

This time there was a near tragedy. When my daughter saw the unmarked bottle, she opened it, inhaled deeply to identify the contents, and almost expired. She couldn't breathe for several frightening seconds and was nearly asphyxiated.

Some brands of ammonia are clear; some are cloudy. The cloudiness certainly doesn't do anything except attempt to deceive you into thinking you are getting something more effective. Actually, neither clarity nor turbidity is an indication of quality. Other types of merchandise try to impress you with their purity because they are crystal clear. This is a lot of hogwash too. Very clear water can be loaded with pathogenic bacteria.

Let me warn you: Do *not* use ammonia when you are using a chlorine bleach at the same time. When you have a detergent which contains ammonia in your washer and you add a chlorine bleach to it, the ammonia releases chlo-

rine gas from the bleach. This is a deadly choking gas that
was used during World War I. This could kill you. A dead
woman can't appreciate how really white her wash is.

Want to hear about something dirty? I'm referring to
soiled clothing, of course. How does something get dirty?
How does the top of your shirt collar get soiled? First, the
oils from the body penetrate the fibers of the shirt. Then
the oils, being sticky, attract the dirt particles much like
a magnet. When you wear a shirt for two or three weeks,
as I do, eventually it's going to have a dirty, gray ring
around the neck and cuffs. Boy, is that dirty and stinky!

In Troy, New York, in 1825, as recorded in Joseph N.
Kane's *Famous First Facts,* Mrs. Hannah Montague re-
belled against washing her husband's shirts so often just
because the collars were dirty. To save labor and soap, she
removed the collars and sewed bands on them that she
could button to the shirt. Soon her friends and neighbors
began to do likewise. This idea started the detachable collar,
so fashionable for over a century.

How does one get rid of this telltale gray ring on shirt
collars? First get rid of the oil, and the dirt comes along
with it. Anything that emulsifies or dissolves the oil will
be a cleaning agent, a detergent. Some people don't like
the smell of ammonia, a good emulsifier, and therefore won't
use it. Besides, like ordinary bleaching, it has a tendency to
change the color of certain dyes.

When water is not used in cleaning we call the process
dry cleaning. Carbon tetrachloride, chlorinated ethylene,
and other organic solvents are the liquids used. All of these
liquid compounds used by professional and amateur dry
cleaners cause the "cleaned" clothing to have a peculiar,
ethereal smell, which can be extremely objectionable.

Since carbon tetrachloride is a dangerous dry-cleaning

liquid, I want to take a few minutes to explain what it may do. Because it is nonflammable, people tend to feel too secure with it and therefore become careless. On the basis of the old idea that hot water is better for washing than cold water, the thought occurs to the woman of the house, "Why not heat the carbon tetrachloride?" This is danger number one. When heated, it is converted into phosgene, another poisonous gas used in warfare. Danger number two is that inhaling the fumes even of unheated carbon tet in a closed room can cause death. One woman who attempted to clean her husband's suit with it in an unventilated room was found slumped over her husband's trousers.

A foolish young girl, ashamed of her excessively oily hair, noticed on the label of a preparation for home cleaning that it was supposed to dissolve grease and oil. Pouring some out into a bowl, she treated herself to a unique shampoo. It provided her with a two-way exit: it was difficult to determine which killed first—the inhaled fumes or the penetration of the poison through her scalp.

A young man, a victim of premature alopecia (baldness), purchased a very expensive hairpiece to soothe his vanity. It was so excellently styled that no one suspected it was not his own hair. To avoid any chance of its slipping out of place, it had to be secured with a harmless adhesive.

However, the glue would build up on the base of the hairpiece, and the unwise young man began removing it, after each wearing, with carbon tet. One morning he was found draped over the tub like a bath mat. Fortunately, he survived, but the doctor warned him to use something less toxic for removing the adhesive thereafter. The carbon tet, which had penetrated his scalp, might finish the job the next time. There are less dangerous solvents for removing spots and adhesives and for general dry cleaning.

7!
The Smell of Repellents and Attractants

MAN IS SUCH A SNOB. While trying desperately to make himself more attractive to his own kind, he resents the intrusion of most lower forms of animal life. Why the elephant and camel were not welcome is easy to see, but there are more than eighty-five thousand species of creeping, crawling, flying unwanted insects not so easy to see.

These creatures never wait to be properly introduced or formally invited before they come to call, so man seeks a scientific method of routing them. Pesticides and insecticides—chemical substances created for the specific purpose of killing—are not the complete answer. It is also essential to find something to make them keep their distance—something to repel them.

Farmers and food-processing firms are always seeking the most effective repellent to use in storage areas and in packaging materials. More money is spent annually on repellents than on perfumes designed to attract.

It is quite a feat to find the most objectionable odors for each undesirable pest. Some of the most successful repellents have odors that are also repulsive to man, yet others seem to have no odor at all. It is simply that they are not detected by the human nose; the little creatures certainly smell them. Insects have a far more sensitive sense of smell than any other form of animal life. A male ant, who smells with his feet, can follow the trail of a female for great distances. He can also follow a trail of sugar into your kitchen. Bees, with twelve thousand scent organs on their antennae, can detect honey at tremendous distances and can classify another bee as kin or foe; but the common moth is the champion of them all. That little air-borne creature, who loves to dine on your best woolens, nose a thing or two.

The most popular mothball, cake, or flake repellent repulses us in the raw state more than it does the moth. We find it necessary to add perfume to the material before compressing it into the common forms. Sometimes I wonder if the perfume doesn't attract rather than repel, because the moths seem to make their annual pilgrimage just the same. Noah missed a good opportunity by not stepping on them when he had the chance.

One of the requirements of moth repellents is that they

should not melt or soften, because that might produce
gummy marks on your clothes. When you stick moth balls
in your coat pockets before you put them away for the
summer, you feel secure that no spots will form because
the repellent changes directly from a solid into a gas. We
call this sublimation. Naphthalene, the substance of which
most moth balls are made, sublimes. In a few weeks you
will find that the moth balls are getting smaller and smaller,
and they finally disappear.

This naphthalene gas is what the moths don't like. One
little whiff through their sniffers and they say in mothenese,
"This place is not for us!" Quickly they travel to other
clothes closets that do not have the repulsive smell.

Recently naphthalene moth balls have been replaced in
considerable measure by other repellents. One, called by
the common name "dichlorocide," smells like a public lavatory. That's one thing I don't like about it. There is no
comfort station like home, but if someone sprinkled dichlorocide in your living room you wouldn't know where you
were. When I smell a lavatory I get ideas, so I don't like
to have the living room or other rooms smelling that way.
Happily, not all people have this reaction. Like naphthalene,
dichlorocide is a white, crystalline solid and it, too, sublimes.

These two repellents are being replaced by far better ones.
Hexylenediol doesn't have much odor for man, but it does
have a repelling effect on the pesky moth. In addition we
have the old-fashioned cedar used to protect woolens in the
off season since the year One. Oil of cedar wood added to
any box will make it into a cedar chest, and the delinquent
little winged destroyers will never know the difference.

"Mosquitoes never bother me." Have you ever heard
that said? There may be a reason for this. It is possible

that those fortunate individuals who are not prone to mosquito attacks have repellents in their skin.

Dr. W. A. Skinner of the Stanford Research Institute in Palo Alto, California, believes that lactic acid, a normal constituent of human sweat, and certain skin fats act as mosquito repellents.

It has been observed that after some types of medication, individuals will not attract mosquitoes. Someday a pill may make you immune to mosquito bites and save you from mosquito-propagated diseases.

Man may soon use acrylic car paints as a weapon in his battle with insects. Sap beetles are especially damaging to growing strawberries. However, it has been found that these beetles will leave their strawberry menu and settle on cars that have been recently retouched or repainted with certain red acrylic paints. One smell can evidently be more attractive than another; so the strawberries are forsaken.

We can repel many types of animals. If you want to chase cucumber beetles, plant spicy nasturtiums in alternating rows (one row cucumbers, one row nasturtiums). When the cucumber beetles come visiting, they don't like the smell of the nasturtiums, so they leave the entire patch. We have told you at the beginning of this book how the smell of camels drives away elephants.

Sometimes we want to get rid of dogs and cats. Now please, don't flare up yet. I know that I have to be very careful because some of you are dog lovers and cat lovers. I am addressing myself to you who love only your *own* furry friend. A neighborhood dog may visit your lawn or some neighborhood cat may work the night shift on your gladioli, and you don't like it. Neither do the gladioli. You may have to put up barriers to keep these "foreign" dogs and cats from your begonias and hedges. Mrs. Smith's

Rover had better not damage the bushes. Your own dog is
all right, you can reason with him.

Spraying the bushes with repellents makes the unwelcome
trespasser go to another bush on some other neighbor's soil
after just one whiff. A dog trusts his nose rather than his
eyes, and when he sniffs a plant, he's really reading the
morning paper. He says, "Who has been here before?" or,
"What's new, Pussycat?" If there's nothing in the "paper"
that he likes, he'll go to some other news stand without
paying his subscription. One preparation for canine repul-
sion contains nicotine sulfate.

That great African general Hannibal, who almost con-
quered powerful Rome, knew the value of animal repellents.
Few know that the elephants that he brought over the Alps
were used not as beasts of burden but to fight with their
trunks swinging, their heads pushing, and their feet crush-
ing the enemy. Their tremendous strength was exceeded
only by their tremendous stench. The enemy's horses were
so terrified by what they smelled, they made a hasty, frantic
retreat. Mother Nature makes her own repellents.

If you are out swimming where there is any possibility
of a shark making an appearance, some authorities suggest
you wear a life jacket containing a special five-ounce bri-
quet prepared for the purpose of repelling the shark. When
the potential killer approaches, you pull a pin to release
a substance that smells like a dead shark. It smells pretty
lousy to the living ones because it warns them of danger.
The sharks vamoose PDQ, so they say.

Birds, although fine feathered friends, frequently must
be kept away, especially at seedtime or cherry-picking time.
It has been a custom since prehistoric days to put a scarecrow in the field or else just to let Uncle Titus stand there,
because birds fear the presence of human beings. If I hang

an old coat of mine out on a pole, the bird that comes near enough to detect my scent will fly away muttering something about that stinky Erb.

Suppose the coat is outside in the field for a number of weeks? Finally, due to the weathering processes, the odor of Erb or Zell or anybody else disappears. Then the birds will actually dare to sit on the scarecrow. To get around this deterioration of scare-smell, chemists have found that if they make a mixture of acrolein (from burnt fat) and old tar (even tar from a pipe) and a little aldehyde with twelve carbon atoms (which smells soapy) and put this mixture on a fence post or a tree out near the garden, the birds will still imagine that there is a human being present, even if they remove the scarecrow. The odor is the repelling factor—not the clothes flapping in the breeze.

The good old summertime is the season of heat, humidity, and chiggers. Nights are romantic with moonlight and biting mosquitoes. Insect repellents must be smeared on copiously to permit humans the dubious pleasure of sitting outdoors, especially at night. Ethyl hexanediol is the active ingredient in some of these repellers of bugs and stinging nuisances. Others contain N, N, diethyl meta toluamide, and with a name like that, it is no wonder the bugs go. Smell repels.

On the other side of the coin, we can produce chemical compounds that will deceive animals into thinking a seasoned mate is in the vicinity. We call these attractants. That's a good name for them. They may be pleasant or unpleasant or possess no smell at all for us. To lower forms of life the specific aroma of an attractant may have an aphrodisiac effect. You see, our mating habits are influenced by odor. Sexual excitation produced by odors is called osmolagnia. Not very romantic, is it? When we fall for a girl or a girl falls for us, we like her aroma and she likes ours. She may not know it consciously but she acts as if she were emotionally affected. "I'll marry this guy; he smells like the marrying kind," she tells herself in no uncertain language, in fact, in no language at all.

We like the smells to which we are accustomed and that's why some people don't get along with others, especially if they have dissimilar backgrounds. Human mating is somewhat dependent on smell. Women often change their natural sex odor by adorning themselves with all sorts of perfumes, that may, hopefully, have sexual implications and complications.

But let's go down to lower species—the animal world, where sex is out in the open. Odoriferous sex glands are highly developed in hoofed animals. The musk deer, for example, is a beautiful animal of Central Asia. The male secretes a substance known as musk from the preputial glands when he feels the mating urge. Mrs. Musk Deer comes a-running on all fours as soon as she gets wind of it. She gets the odorous message. If you are a rat-fink you can bring a female musk deer running your way merely by spraying some musk on yourself, but you'll alienate all the male musk deer in the community. Musk is quite expensive. The active principle in it is muscone, which can now be produced synthetically in the laboratory. In the right concentration it smells gloriously pleasing to man, but not so in the natural undiluted state.

Other animals, such as an African feline known as a civet cat, have similar love-making devices. Both sexes of this species have glands that secrete a substance that is a powerful attractant for the opposite sex. The male produces a greater quantity. Man has removed these glands from the civet cat to obtain a yellow, gummy, solid mass which he uses as a fixative in some exceptional perfumes. We are trying to utilize these attractant secretions from animals in the hope that when the woman wears the aroma, the man of her choice will feel a certain love-potion attraction. Whether it works or not, I don't know. We get married, none the less.

The industrious little beaver, who dams up lakes and streams to the consternation of fishermen and is valued by furriers for his handsome pelts, is also highly regarded by perfume chemists. He secretes an ugly, malodorous substance from his pineal gland called castor or castoreum. This brownish-orange exudate, which is repulsively pungent when concentrated and pleasantly fragrant when diluted, is used as a fixative.

Little Miss Beatrice Beaver, out on a hunting trip with her new fur coat on, glides gracefully along the edge of the sylvan pool laced with wild flowers, admiring her own reflection now and then, when suddenly she catches a whiff of Bobby Beaver's castoreum. They meet, are romantically united, and live happily ever after; at least as long as the custom prevails. It is as alluring to her as it is to the cosmetician, but for a far different reason.

One summer, a number of years ago, when we experienced an unusually destructive infestation of Japanese beetles, agricultural researchers catalogued the types of vegetation most sought after by the little darlings. Number one on the hit parade by a big margin was the geranium. Well, you can guess the result. Right away beetle traps were prepared containing oil of geranium as bait. The unsuspecting insects congregated on this unusual source of their favorite smell, thinking they were in for a delicious meal, but they were only in for it—period. An attractant may be appealing or appalling, depending on whose viewpoint you are considering. When the trap became filled, some people dumped the beetles out and stepped on them or burned them or annihilated them in other sadistic ways. Some, in good sportsman fashion, merely took off the lid and let them fly away. They were chicken and wanted to give the beetles a second chance.

Mother Nature has mysterious ways of attracting lower forms of life that have absolutely no appeal to man. For half a century a farmer raised pigs on a ninety-acre tract of land about fifteen miles outside Philadelphia. Until a few years ago, no neighbor was in the general vicinity. Then a real-estate developer bought the surrounding land and erected hundreds of little boxes made of ticky-tacky that all looked the same but were called ranch houses.

It was no coincidence that they were completed and sold during the winter, when odor doesn't travel very well. Because the piggery was not visible from the road, no one mentioned it. Came spring, followed by summer, followed by humidity, and the porcine population advertised its whereabouts with very noxious certainty. The new tenants got the message when an ominous bank of vapors, impelled by a strong breeze, drifted toward the houses. Though the smell was repulsive to the home owners, it was very attractive to rodents, flies, bees, and mosquitoes, who didn't believe in staying in just one place.

For forty-six years, no one but the farmer knew that the insects were so attracted by his little friends. His new neighbors tried to force the farmer by legal means to move his piggery elsewhere or discontinue his business in that neighborhood. The State Health Authorities found conditions sufficiently hygienic, and with increased use of insecticides and rodenticides, he stood firm.

A tisket, a tasket, a quota of fish in a basket! Never

again do you need to come home from a fishing trip empty creeled. Nor do you have to cheat by purchasing some fish from a market 'ere you face the little woman (42–34–42). Before you leave, à la Izaak Walton, just get a bottle of the new sure-lure fish scent, "guaranteed" to appeal to all salt- and fresh-water fish. Apply it to a little adhesive pad which fits snugly on the hook for sensational results. You will simply amaze your friends, the ad reads, but your wife will run away from home when she sees all the work you have brought her.

Man's inefficient olfaction has been his salvation. He never really learned to appreciate the true worth of decaying matter. The repulsiveness of it made him clean up the dirty place that caused the stench. He even thought foul odors spread illness because patients suffering from epidemic diseases such as smallpox, typhus, and diphtheria were malodorous.

The house mosquito, which is a potential encephalitis carrier, is able to distinguish certain odors according to entomologists E. I. Hazard and M. S. Mayer, and technician K. E. Savage, all of American Cyanamid. Mosquitoes are attracted to water because of the odor given off by bacteria and bacterial products. It is hoped that a product will be developed that by its odor will attract mosquitoes to designated areas, where the pests will be eliminated.

Man's olfactory perceptiveness is so short-scented that he cannot detect the presence of a female until she comes close enough to see and to touch. It may be too late then. Generally this is good because he wants to see what he is getting—like going to a cafeteria.

Olfactory deception is achieved by canceling or masking offensiveness. The redolent resins of cedar wood banish mustiness in a closet, just as the oriental bouquet of incense provides a highly diffusive coverage for almost any stench. Archeologists claim that when the tombs of ancient kings are opened for the first time in centuries, the incense therein still overpowers the effluvium of the decayed monarch and his beasts, birds, flies, and bats. Its persistence is uncanny. However, some odors are as impossible to obliterate as a thumbprint.

The world of chemistry has gone hog-wild trying to devise new ways of covering up that which we do not wish to smell. Just check the shelf containing such products in your supermarket and you will know what I mean.

Instead of simply putting insecticides, repellents, or attractants on the trees or on the bushes to keep them protected, chemists may use a substance called dimethyl sulfoxide, DMSO, which is a liquid with excellent solvent powers. When an insecticide or repellent has been dissolved in it, and it is put on a plant or a tree, it diffuses through the entire plant structure, acting as a permanent repellent for the growing plant. The medical profession is experimenting with DMSO as a solvent for medications, but it is still considered unsafe for human use. An unusual property of DMSO is that it affects man's taste and smell by remote control. For example, when a small quantity is applied to the feet, it is soon absorbed into the circulatory system. Within a short time, the subject's mouth will taste like oysters. This might be a new way to get the pleasure of an oyster stew taste without buying oysters. This is not too bad, but after a while, he'll have a garlic breath. This is smelling, not by the nasal avenue, but by the blood route.

Years ago automobile tires made with synthetic rubber had holes chewed in them by hungry rats. That was a disappointing thing to discover when you went to your parked car in the morning. The manufacturer found it necessary to formulate a new synthetic rubber that was not attractive to rodents. You can be a modern Pied Piper: A good way of luring rodents from your property to your neighbor's acres is to throw a few pieces of synthetic rubber into the yard next door. This is the good neighbor policy in reverse and it could do the trick. A liquid smelling like synthetic rubber can be produced in the laboratory. A rat poison mixed with such a smelly liquid would attract them to their last meal.

8!
The Smell of Danger

A CONVENIENT PROTECTION furnished by Nature is that many of the poisonous, dangerous things that you encounter in your daily walk through life have an objectionable odor. Now that's very, very good. If everything that is actually poisonous smelled pleasant, many of you would be dead, and the sale of this book would drop off. Deadly nerve gases, probably still being produced by our government for warfare emergencies, are deliberately made odorless to avoid detection by means of smell. The first indications that such a gas is present are symptoms of mental disturbance or maybe death. The latter is a bad symptom. Just as harmful vapors are usually malodorous, nature also gives dangerous vegetation an evil flavor. No self-respecting animal would taste anything without giving it the nostril test first. Mankind take a warning!

Though some like the unique pungency of gasoline, its odor is certainly an attention-getter. Its distinctive smell warns that it is toxic and flammable. Used as a cleaning fluid, it can blast you into orbit with no re-entry program. Benzine, another fraction of petroleum, acts similarly. Both could be made odorless, but that would be dangerous.

Personally, I like the smell of gasoline—it is intoxicating. That is why service-station attendants are always so happy and want to clean your windshield over and over again. They may be half drunk.

When I was in college we held "naphtha jags" when no one was around. We would heat a brick on the kitchen stove, then take it to a little room where we placed on it a pan containing a very small quantity of gasoline. After a few minutes the vapors produced a very exhilarating effect. This practice is not recommended, because it can be very harmful to the liver and nervous system.

Lighter fluid has an ethereal odor, as it should have, because it is dangerously flammable. A warning smell! It is sometimes handled quite carelessly, especially when open flames are nearby.

The same thing applies to the warning odor of nail-polish remover. Most polish removers are flammable, but women frequently smoke while using them. What would milady do if her fingers burst into flame? The better-grade removers use nonflammable solvents as well as perfumes to give them osmic appeal.

Turpentine, which has the resinousness of a pine tree, may cause harmful side effects to certain individuals, but the warning smell advises such people to leave for a pure atmosphere—like the elephants.

Our schools should teach students how to identify the odors of poisons. Everyone should know how carbolic acid smells. Suppose someone gave you fruit that reeked of carbolic acid; you should know enough to refuse it, and discard it. If you inhale kerosene, you would not recognize it unless you've been advised of its identity previously. You must be taught how to identify the unfamiliar. Right between your eyes and your mouth is a marvelous instrument for detecting whether something is good or bad. You may pick up a hunk of meat that is tainted, but before you take it into your mouth, you smell it and know that it should not be eaten.

Yes, the nose is important. Everyone should have one.

One smelly substance that may cause death is a compound called hydrocyanic acid. It has been the official means of execution in some states. It is the favorite tool for homicide in murder mysteries. The authors usually call it Prussic acid. It has an odor of bitter almonds.

If you come home and find Aunt Fanny lying on the floor with her mouth open (you know it's Aunt Fanny because her mouth is always open), stoop down and smell her open mouth. If you detect the scent of bitter almonds, you are a detective and can say, "Ah! Aunty died of HCN." This won't help Aunt Fanny, but it might help you and law enforcement officials in tracking down the culprit. Smell is important as a warning, as a diagnostic sign, and as a suggested course of treatment. It is essential that we have these signals inculcated in our memory so that we can always identify them in time.

I have always believed that an odor-identification kit should be made available to those people born sightless. Such a kit should consist of bottles with droppers containing various dangerous odoriferous materials in simulated, nontoxic, harmless liquid form. For example, a benign liquid smelling like gasoline would be in a bottle labeled in Braille. By placing a drop of this liquid on a piece of paper toweling or facial tissue, the sightless person could learn to recognize the smell of gasoline for future identification. This might be repeated with other liquids simulating the smell of carbon tetrachloride, illuminating gas, chlorine, etc. Such "smell libraries" would be used for reference and as a nose-sensory refresher.

During wartime, civil defense agencies put out a war-gas identification kit. The idea was to teach noncombatants and civilians how to know the odor of poisonous war gases such as mustard gas, Lewisite, etc.

It seems that by using our nose and smelling mechanism, we may be able to detect temperature changes. I have found that I can do this. It is known that heat gives rise to a certain odor sensation. I can tell when someone is using an electric iron in another part of the house. I may be sitting in my comfortable English lounge chair, drinking beer, or just inhaling air if I'm out of beer, when my wife silently turns on the electric iron two rooms away from me. I can definitely smell when the iron gets hot. Heat stimulates a peculiar sensation of smell. Why? Could it be due to the electrons that are given off by the hot metal?

The smell sensation also records coldness. Perhaps at one time you have stepped into a large refrigerated room, such as is found in meat packing plants or in wine cellars, and experienced the nose reaction to sudden coldness? Even though no other odor is present, cold air can be detected nasally.

During one of my TV programs, when I was talking about this smell-reaction to heat and cold, a viewer called in to state that he could smell an oncoming snowfall (in winter only, of course). Others said they could predict rain by their smell sensations. This is undoubtedly true; some people possess extrasensory smell perception, ESSP.

A probable explanation for these smell forecasts lies in the falling or rising barometric pressure, which makes the earth inhale and exhale just like an animal. Under high pressure, a certain quantity of vapors become entrapped and stagnant within the porous spaces of the earth's soil. When this atmospheric pressure drops, these vapors are released and we then smell the exhaled moist air from the soil. As the air ascends, the leaves seem to turn up, revealing their under side, a condition we recognize as a sign of an approaching storm. Since low pressure is associated with unpleasant weather, rain in summer and snow in winter, the smeller of these rising vapors becomes a forecaster. This method might be an improvement over our present TV weather forecasts, which contain more questionable humor than precipitation accuracy.

Closely related to heat is the smell of fire and burning material. The smell of a burning mattress, for instance, has been imprinted in the sensory memory areas of most of our fire-fighting men, because so many house fires are started by people smoking in bed. The rule should be: "Don't smoke in bed; the ashes you get on the floor may be your own." But this advice is taken lightly. It's like telling an American Indian to see America first.

Other scents we should all be able to recognize are those

of paper burning and a smoking electrical insulator or socket. Yes, these are important warning smells. The acridness of overheating and burning prompts me to action. Should I get up to turn off that electric iron while my wife is phoning, or relatively speaking? Or should I let it alone and allow the ironing board to catch on fire, then the house, then collect the insurance?

Speaking of insurance, years ago I knew a man who was selling fire insurance. When a client's premium was due, he sent out a letter urging the customer to renew his policy, enclosing a picture of a home with red flames coming out of the windows. "Mail your check without delay," the caption read. A chemical in the red ink smelled like burning wood in the hope that the checks would come in faster. When Titus Zell started opening his mail, he was quite relaxed. Then he started sniffing! Suddenly he stiffened, shouting, "Oh Gladys, my fire insurance is due. We better renew it today. I smell something burning now!"

Of course, the United States Post Office wouldn't want all sorts of odoriferous things put in the mail. Something mailed that possesses smell should be encased in an impermeable inner envelope that will hold the odor within its confines until the reader opens the epistle.

Now we come to another of the warning smells—the moldy smell. Whenever we detect a fungal mustiness, we should realize that some of our household's worldly goods are being destroyed. Maybe books are being consumed, maybe some clothing.

Mildew is a plant that grows by throwing out very slender filaments. Fungicides are chemicals that stop or kill the growth of fungi, such as mildew. Since you wouldn't want to use a fungicide that smelled worse than the mold, the unpleasantness must be discreetly masked.

Another way to get rid of mildew is to have the room dry, since the mildew plants need moisture for their growth and existence. Out-of-season shoes and other garments are often stored in tightly sealed plastic bags to keep out moisture and moths. This is excellent providing the stored articles were absolutely dry when sealed. If there is any moisture on the soles of the shoes, for instance, don't be surprised to find them all mildewed when you retrieve them. A good brushing and airing may be sufficient to restore them. The manufacturers of paradichlorocide, the moth repellent, claim that it will also control mildew. Perhaps a little of this should be placed in the bag before sealing.

Though most harmful gases have a perceptible odor, some few gases that are poisonous have no odor at all. For example, you cannot smell carbon monoxide. This is one of the deadliest gases you are likely to meet, and sometimes you only meet it once. The first symptom of carbon monoxide poisoning is a feeling as if you had been hit on the head, and then comes unconsciousness. You can't do anything about it after that. Something malodorous must be added for our protection. In many communities a number of years ago, odorless carbon monoxide gas was piped right into the kitchens for cooking purposes. It was a suicide agent delivered to the home, and there may still be places where it is used. There is always the hazard of accidentally turning a valve and not being able to detect the leak. Since carbon monoxide is generated by your car, let me again warn you, although you have heard this warning over and over: Never run the motor of your car in a closed garage. It will be your last run.

Artificially produced illuminating gas can be made odorless or even pleasant, but the law demands that certain substances be added to give it an alerting, easily identifiable olfaction. One must in*stink*tively know when a valve is leaking.

The type of odorant used should be uniform throughout the nation but it isn't. I am well acquainted with that employed in Pennsylvania, but one time, when traveling in another state, I was nearly asphyxiated. The home in which I visited was heated by little gas stoves in each room. One afternoon when I entered my room, it was highly perfumed with a fragrance that I couldn't recognize. After some time its persistence annoyed me so I asked my hostess what it was. She ran to the heater, turned off the valve, opened the windows, and said it was gas. She apologized for the impractical "joke" of her little son, a lovable brat.

Such additives are sometimes called re-odorants, i.e., preparations that are used to odorize an otherwise odorless thing or even person. They either change an odor or add odor where previously none existed. Some are pleasant but the unpleasant re-odorants are the ones often used in odorless poisonous gases as a warning agent.

The story is told that the Bureau of Mines was experimenting in trying to detect a leak in a certain gas main in a residential section. Without announcing it to the consumers, they put a highly odoriferous material in the gas, a chemical called a mercaptan. Mercaptans are foul-smelling substances, even worse than skunk oil or dead, decaying, ignored cabbage. Now when the home occupants turned on the gas, they smelled this objectionable, putrid odor, with very peculiar reactions. One man went back to his butcher and returned the steak he had recently purchased, claiming he had been sold rotten meat. He blamed the stink on the butcher. A wife threw out all her husband's shoes. Another wife insisted that her husband take a bath. The reactions were different but the whole community was up in arms about this mysterious, fetid smell. They thought surely something dead or decaying was on the premises.

These compounds called mercaptans are organic compounds that have sulfur in them. The symbol "S" stands for the element sulfur. We put an "H" after it and we will put certain things in front of it such as the methyl group, written CH_3 in chemical formulation. Then this specific mercaptan CH_3SH would be called methyl mercaptan. If an ethyl group were attached to the SH group it would be called ethyl mercaptan.

Mercaptans are, as a rule, powerfully stinky substances. I made some when I was an undergraduate student at college. I won't mention the college; they might recall my diploma. One uncomfortable day late in May, I was working in the organic chemistry laboratory with other students. We were tired of working on routine procedures, so we thought we would try a novel experiment that was not found in the cookbook known unaffectionately as the laboratory manual. We made a mercaptan. Very carefully we sealed it in a glass tube or ampule. After this was done, we watched to see if the coast would clear. Our lab was on the second floor of the building. Outside below our windows there was a concrete sidewalk. Across the campus quadrangle there were other classes in session in buildings holding perspiring students. It was a hot, humid day with a slight whisper of a breeze blowing away from the chemistry building.

Unnoticed, we dropped the glass ampule out of the window. When it hit the sidewalk target, it broke, releasing the mercaptan vapor, which then gradually permeated one building after another. We saw classes being dismissed all over the place with the professors often in the front ranks and on the double. We had to go out too to avoid suspicion.

Everybody looked at the other person and thought, "Did you do it, or did he do it?" A good idea when something smells bad is to blame it on the other guy.

I know of a similar case, in which a vial containing allyl alcohol, a tear gas, was used. The unscrupulous carrier rode on a bus and sat in the very last seat (I almost said pew). He slyly put a few drops of the alcohol on the floor. The first reaction was from the woman across the aisle (men always sit across from women across the aisle), who began wiping her eyes. She looked at the man, so he wiped his eyes too. No use giving his secret away. When the odor diffused forward to the next seat, those riders also wiped their eyes. By the time the bus reached its terminus, the driver was weeping all over the place. Odors will diffuse and affect large numbers of people. This, we will say, was the purpose of this experiment, but don't try it because it's illegal, and I'm sorry that I told you how I did it.

Acid! The word strikes fear in most people's minds. They have heard so many tales about being burnt with acid, about acid being thrown by people with homicidal tendencies, and about drinking acids by mistake. It is true that we should have a certain amount of respect for some of the common acids, such as sulfuric and nitric acid, especially when they are concentrated. Another common acid is hydrochloric acid. It is found in your stomach all of the time, but you are not afraid of it because it is dilute and it is necessary for you to go on living.

Something not usually known is that most acids are white solids and are not harmful to us. In truth, many of them are of great benefit.

The common liquid acids have pungent "acid" smells—vinegary in nature. This should be a warning smell and should make you suspicious.

When fruit juices are permitted to ferment, they pass first to the alcohol stage. This change is brought about in the presence of oxygen or air, and the resultant substance is wine—or hard cider if apple juice was used. If now more air comes in contact with the fermenting wine, oxidation of the alcohol of the wine changes it to acid—acetic acid or vinegar. The smell tells. To prevent the alcohol from fermenting into acid vinegar, the bottle must be kept well stoppered to exclude air. All persons should be able to identify the acid smell—the sour smell. It may tell you if something has gone bad.

Aspirin is an acid. It is called acetylated salicylic acid. Next time ask for it by name, if you can. The drug clerk may say he's out of it. It is really made up of two different acids. One of these acids is called salicylic acid, a white crystalline powder. In medical practice it is known as a keratolytic agent, meaning that when used cautiously and externally in solutions of 1 to 10 per cent, it can remove corns, calluses, warts, and dermal growths of like nature. It is a very corrosive acid when in solution. The other acid is acetic acid, which is the acid found in a diluted condition in vinegar. When these two acids get together chemically, an acetylated salicylic acid is produced. This is what makes up an aspirin tablet, no matter what the brand name. Since the Food and Drug Administration regulates the content of anything so labeled, one type of aspirin is identical with another. It is foolish to assume that one particular kind is superior because the brand name is widely advertised.

When aspirin tablets meet moisture, as when the bottle is opened and closed frequently in a damp atmosphere, the water hydrolyzes the drug and splits it into its two component acids. The acetic acid has a distinct vinegary, acid smell. The salicylic acid is practically odorless. Check the bottle you have in your medicine cabinet or the kitchen cupboard. If it smells like vinegar, throw it away, because it will no longer help you. What you're really doing then is swallowing a corn remedy and no respectable stomach should stomach that. The buffered type of aspirin may neutralize the free acids formed and the vinegary smell will not be apparent to warn you.

9!
A Theory of How We Smell

It is my belief that the sensation of smell is electrical in nature. If this is so, you may have Smellovision at some future time. Right in your own home you may tune in a TV channel to smell as well as hear and see your favorite program. At present you are saved a lot of heartaches because you can't smell certain things in the studio. In the future perhaps you may be able not only to view a home show, but to smell the frying egg or hamburger as well. Think of how this could be exploited in commercials. It might be bad for witnessing wrestling matches, especially the tight shots. In multifamily homes where there are several sets, each tuned to a different channel, the effect could be scentsational!

There are at least three conditions necessary before a substance creates an odor. It may smell like a skunk, or a rose, whichever you prefer, but before the sensation gets into your "think tank," something has to happen.

The odoriferous material must be vaporizable or volatile. Scientists do not use the word *vaporizable* (it's too understandable)—they say *volatile*. If it's not volatile it can't reach your nasal apparatus. If a substance vaporizes very rapidly, the odor does not last too long. Only those that vaporize slowly are durable.

When these odors are wafted abroad, they must have enough vapor pressure to reach your nose if you are to recognize them. A hunk of wood can't be smelled from a distance because it doesn't produce long-traveling wood gas. Its vapor pressure is low. Maybe if you'd get down on all fours, you could smell the floor by sniffing. Solids and liquids must be able to pass into the gaseous state in order to be osmically appreciated. How does this volatile vapor get to your nose? It must be air-borne; it must be sniffable. If ammonia is put on a wad of cotton in one part of the room, it soon fills the entire room. There is a transmission of odoriferous particles from the source to the nose by the process known as diffusion. Things that have a strong or pungent smell diffuse very rapidly. If they diffuse slowly, the odor will last much longer but will lack pungency.

As we explained in an earlier chapter, we exercise our ability to smell by both inhalation and exhalation. Whether we sniff externally or force the odor-rich air from our mouth upward, we are accomplishing the same final result—the odor vapors are reaching our olfactory sensory areas in the nostrils.

The nasal passages must be kept open for the most efficient intake of odor-rich particles. When one experiences a common cold, mucous discharges frequently cause a blockage that seriously interferes with normal smelling. The moist, oily surface of the passages attracts dust particles, which are being inhaled constantly. Instead of being blown right out again when we exhale, this dust just dries right where it is imprisoned.

Dirt that accumulates under the nails is called gomé. You knew that didn't you? The waste that accumulates in other localities of the body has specific names, but no matter how or where I searched, I could find no name for these little, dried masses of dust in the nose. As a biochemist, for many years I have felt it my duty to rectify this oversight by coining the word *rhinoconite* (pronounced rī nok' o nīte). This name is derived from the Greek, *rhino,* meaning nose, and *conium,* meaning dust, with the suffix *ite* to denote an association or massing. I taught this word to thousands of my students. Now you too can tell anyone who asks you, if they ever do, that the accumulation of dirt in your nose is a rhinoconite. Pick it!

It seems that odorous substances should be soluble in water and/or in fatty material. If a substance is soluble in both water and fat, it is likely to be more odorous than if it is soluble only in water. There are, however, exceptions to the principle that effective odorants must be soluble in both water and fat. Acetone is not extremely soluble in fat, yet it has a strong odor.

It may be that the combined liquids found in the nasal tract and receptor cells produce a solvent not at all like a water and/or fat solvent. In fact, there is some evidence that a protein solution may be the solvent for odorants. The mucus lining of the nostrils, the fatty substances of the cells of the nerve endings, and the proteinaceous fluids that are ever present may together constitute the special nasal solvent.

Finally, in order to be odoriferous, the chemical substance, which has by now reached the nerve endings of the nose, must have the capacity for being oxidized or reduced. Oxidation is a loss of electrons and reduction is a gain of electrons. Both processes must occur simultaneously. Reactions of this type are known as reduction-oxidation or *redox*. There could be an electron transfer taking place in your nose, and this, we believe, is the beginning of the smell sensation as an electrical stimulus. The electrical impulses transmit the odor messages to the brain. These electrical impulses are produced, we believe, by the oxygen of the air oxidizing the vapor we have inhaled. The oxidation is especially speeded up by enzymes, which are organic catalysts made by the body. They are proteins and their mere presence causes the speed-up of a reaction.

What are enzymes like? A school teacher may act as an enzyme or catalyst. Her mere presence in the classroom may speed up the written assignments done during the class period. The teacher may leave the room and immediately there is talking, horseplay, and general inattentiveness until the teacher returns. She need not say a word. Her being there in the room restores a better atmosphere for orderliness and learning. Some of the best teachers are good catalysts—good enzymes.

In the Lancaster area of Pennsylvania, where the Amish brethren still use the horse and buggy as a means of transportation, the whip in the socket acts as a catalyst. When it is rattling, the horse runs normally. Now when the young Amisher who is taking his "girl" for a ride wishes the horse to travel more leisurely, he simply removes the whip from the whip socket. The horse slows down, the lad increases his activities, and a good time is had by all, including the horse.

Enzymes, the organic catalysts, are intimately concerned with our body functions. Our living would not be possible without our suite of highly specific enzymes. The fact that you can breathe at all today, and I hope you can, is made possible by enzymes called oxidases. When you eat meat, it has to be digested to have any nutritive value. Pepsin, an enzyme in the stomach, and trypsin, an enzyme in the intestinal canal, bring about the digestion in short order, at least in time for your next meal. Other enzymes are responsible for blood clotting, which prevents you from bleeding to death every time you suffer a cut or a scratch. (Of course, you can bleed to death only once.)

In the nerve endings of the nose there are enzymes—the oxidases, the reductases, and the peroxidases. The olfactory regions, those parts of the nose where the sensory organs of smell lie, are about the size of United States postage stamps (regular, not commemorative size). There are two such areas, one found at the upper end of each nostril. They are of yellow color and are rich in moisture and fatty substances.

Just as heredity determines the size, shape, and color of all the other parts of your body, so does it influence the shade of yellow of the olfactory region. The deeper and more intense the shade, the keener the sense of smell. Albinos have very feeble osmic powers. This is true of both men and lower forms of animal life.

The pigment in macrosmatic animals, animals with a

highly developed sense of smell, is darker than in man. While in man the olfactory pigment is light yellow, the cat has a deep yellow-brown and the fox, a reddish-brown. Dark-skinned men have a darker olfactory pigmentation and therefore should be expected to have a greater acuity of smell. It is said that Arabs can smell a fire thirty miles away, even on a breezeless day.

Closely related to the pigment of the olfactory tract are the Bowman glands, which secrete a pigmented fluid to keep the olfactory area constantly covered and lubricated. This glandular secretion is brown in the dog, reddish-brown in the rabbit, and dark brown to black in sheep. In man, Bowman's gland secretion is replaced by the clear secretion of the mucous glands.

It is in man's yellow olfactory spots that the enzymes of oxidation and reduction are concentrated. There they accelerate the rate of oxidation of odorous gases with the oxygen of the inhaled air.

An electrical impulse is produced. That is the stimulus that makes you differentiate fried onions from oil of lavender. This may be shocking news. These electrical charges are self-generated, and are instantaneously produced when the odor vapor strikes the sensory area. It is the *change* in electrical charges that is perceptible. When it is unchanging and in a state of equilibrium, we no longer smell. This is called odor fatigue.

You cannot always rely on your nose to determine what kind of an olfactory imprint you are making. The female of the species may be boiling cabbage or, worse yet, sauerkraut for dinner. The house is full of it (the smell, not the kraut). Hubby comes home from work, or so he claims, and the minute he enters the door he yells, "Phew, sauerkraut again," or "Oh boy, we're having sauerkraut tonight!" Wifey says she can't smell a thing except his aromatic pipe.

She is nonreactive to the first odoriphore because she has experienced it for some time but alert to the second because it is newly introduced. It is the reverse for him. Let's hope they find the change mutually agreeable.

Odor fatigues may be a blessing if you have to work in an unpleasant atmosphere like a fertilizer plant or a rubber-tire factory. It can also be very dangerous if you are exposed to a poisonous gas. The vapor may be introduced so gradually you are not aware of its presence until, suddenly, it is too late. Next day you make the headlines with a simple line: "Overcome by Gas."

If it can be proved that smell is electrical in nature, then we should be able to transmit it by electronic means. We should be able to go to the smellophone and say, "How alluring you smell today!" instead of just plain "Hello." The woman might say, "Can you smell me? I'm all perspired." Or, "Just smell the place. That Avon lady was here." She could even ask, "Does this smell as if I put enough spice in my chili?" The possibilities are infinite. Don't laugh. They laughed at Edison, Fulton, and Hinkeldreck. In the latter case, it was the name that made them laugh.

"Flowers Delivered by Telegram" may someday be amended to read, "Floral Odors by Smellophone."

Among other physical properties of odorous matter that have been given some attention is the way in which odorants react to light: absorption, refraction, scattering, etc. For instance, odoriferous solutions strongly absorb infrared waves. Similar absorption in the ultraviolet region of the electromagnetic spectrum has been noted. Many liquids, odorants or not, have the ability to change the wave length of monochromatic light shining through them so that it emerges with a different wave length. This difference is known as the Raman shift. It is claimed that only the odorous substances have shifts between 140 mμ and 350 mμ.

There is apparently no definite relationship between odor and the chemical composition of the odorant. Some compounds with a great difference in composition smell alike, while others of similar structure and composition smell different.

Odorous substances belong largely in the field of organic chemistry, i.e., the chemistry of the carbon compounds, rather than inorganic chemistry. They are relatively complex in constitution. Some of the organic compounds do change their odor depending on the number of carbon atoms they contain. We have a class of organic compounds called aldehydes. Although the aldehyde group (–CHO) is the same in all of them, the total number of carbon atoms in each may be different. The odor apparently changes as the number of carbon atoms changes. Thus, an 8-carbon aldehyde has a honey-like odor; a 9-carbon aldehyde, a rosy-orange odor; 10 carbons, soapy; 14 carbons, peachy; 16 carbons, strawberry; 18 carbons, toasted coconut; 19 carbons, pineapple; and 20 carbons, raspberry.

Finding the composition of odoriferous vapors was and still is a difficult analysis to accomplish. Knowing the raspberry-smelling aldehyde has twenty carbon atoms has made it possible to duplicate the aroma. The nose is still the most accurate scientific instrument in odor analysis, but other instruments are now being used to analyze odorant vapors.

By the use of gas chromatography, complex odors can now be analyzed directly. For instance, a sample of the vapor from a freshly opened can of coffee can be drawn into a vapor fractometer and its aroma analyzed. Flavor chemists have noted at least 125 components in strawberries. As we increase our knowledge of odors, more practical applications of synthetic aromatization can be made.

In inorganic chemistry, none of the elements that are found in nature has an odor in its free state. When combined, many of these odorless elements form compounds with marked odors. For example, hydrogen and sulfur both occur free or uncombined in nature; neither element has an odor by itself, but combining them produces a gas called hydrogen sulfide that smells like rotten eggs. The halogen family of elements—chlorine, bromine, iodine, and fluorine —do not occur normally in their atomic or free state; but in their diatomic state—as Cl_2, Br_2, I_2, and F_2—they do have a strong pungent odor. Phosphorus has an odor in the yellow allotropic form, P_4. Oxygen has an odor in the molecular form of ozone, O_3. The element arsenic yields a garlic-like smell only upon heating.

Our sense of smell, although quite keen, is not developed or exercised as it should be. It is said that dogs are osmically more sensitive than their masters, but I think the latter's ability has been underestimated. I'd like to do an experiment in which a student would hold on to the axle of a wheel (like the front of a wheelbarrow) and someone else would grab him by the legs and wheel him over our athletic field. I believe, with a little training, he could pinpoint where the first down was made, or where the ball went out of bounds, because his nose would be nearer to the ground. That may be one of the reasons dogs smell things we cannot—we're too far away from the source. The question is how can we keep our nose to the ground and to the grind-stone at the same time?

And so to bed between clean-smelling sheets. Chase your camels and troubles away and tether the elephants. And phew to you, and you, and you!

Postface

I HAVE always hated prefaces. They seem to get in the way when you are ready to read a book. In most cases, prefaces are skipped over entirely, so why not a Postface?

After you have gotten through the printed pages, if you haven't liked the book, you will be in doubt as to why in heaven's name it was written in the first place. On the other hand, if you really enjoyed the book you may want to go on reading; so here, for your added enjoyment, is the Postface.

Smell has always been of interest to me, because I have been told I do. The more I studied the few works dealing with smell, and the more I associated with different aromatic people, the more my interest was aroused. As an organic chemist, I found many compounds that possessed odor but could only be described or dismissed as being "characteristic." What was more disturbing, the literature of organic chemistry contained very little or no reference at all to the odors of compounds. Properties such as density, color, solubility, etc., were listed in great detail, but nary a word as to smell.

Then when I began lecturing weekly on the University of the Air (on the ABC Television Network), one of my most popular series was devoted to osmics, the science of smell. The viewers lifted their noses, they got the scent, and their postal response was most gratifying. Later the National Broadcasting Company suggested that I produce a series of Educational Exchange Films on "Smell Sells." These videotapes were shown all over the United States. They again brought forth such a response that it was evident the viewing public was actively interested in problems involving smell. Radio participation programs stimulated similar reactions.

Numerous viewers wrote to me expressing a desire to purchase a copy of my "book," which I had hinted at on the series. Little did they know all the programs had been strictly ad-lib with not one word in black and white.

The suggestion that I really write a book was put to me so often, I finally succumbed. I had the tapes, so why not start from there? This little book is the result.

Although it may appear humorous, it is, nevertheless, authoritatively based on my more than twenty years of study and research. It is purposely written in the style it is to make it easily understood by everyone. It is meant to stimulate a greater interest in the science of osmics.

I must give credit to my wife, who is referred to occasionally and who helped to make this book possible by giving me money to buy a typewriter ribbon and enough paper.

I also want to, and I will, give a certain amount of credit to my boxer, "Stinky," who inspired me in many nasal ways.

A girl at College, Miss Gwen H. Sweney, offered to type the script. Her mistakes in typing improved the copy greatly.

If you have enjoyed this book, why not buy a copy for yourself?

RUSSELL C. ERB

References

Amoore, John E. Private communications.

Bienfang, Ralph. *The Subtle Sense.* Norman: University of Oklahoma Press, 1946.

Geldard, Frank A. *The Human Senses.* New York: John Wiley, 1953.

McCord, C. P., and W. N. Witheridge. *Odors, Physiology and Control.* New York: McGraw-Hill, 1949.

Moncrieff, R. W. *The Chemical Senses.* New York: John Wiley, 1946.

Tucker, Don. "Physical Variables in the Olfactory Stimulating Process," *Journal of General Physiology,* 1963.

I have also found the following periodicals to be invaluable:

American Perfumer and Cosmetics.

Chemical Abstracts.

Essential Oil Review.

Fritzsche Brothers, Inc. Bulletins and Handbook.

Givaudanian, Industrial Aromatics Division. Bulletins.

Sindar Reporter.